Till That Day Comes

Based on a True Story

by

Kelly D. McManus

PROFESSIONAL PUBLISHING MEETS POWERFUL PROMOTION

A wholly owned subsidiary of TBN

Till That Day Comes

Trilogy Christian Publishers A Wholly Owned Subsidiary of Trinity Broadcasting Network

2442 Michelle Drive Tustin, CA 92780

Manufactured in the United States of America

10 9 8 7 6 5 4 3 2 1

Library of Congress Cataloging-in-Publication Data is available.

ISBN: 978-1-63769-458-9

E-ISBN: 978-1-63769-459-6

For my loving Abba Father, who always saw the potential in me, even while I rolled around in my mess. You never ceased to spur me on or pour out your grace to weave the words you prepared in advance for me to write. Thank you, *Till That Day Comes* and beyond.

Contents

Contents

Foreword

"*Till That Day Comes* helps answer common questions about why God allows suffering. I'm honored that God used The Back to God Hour to help share that lesson and that Kelly McManus has told this story in a new and interesting way."

Kurt Seles
Director ReFrame Ministries
(formerly The Back to God Hour)

"I had the immense privilege of knowing Sara Schreck. As a healthy teenager, she was goofy, fun, and loud. As a teenager with cancer, she was still goofy and fun, but it was then that God amplified her life and her voice to absolutely thunderous levels. I'm grateful for Kelly's book because now you can meet Sara too. More importantly, you will meet God in the way Sara did. This is an unforgettable story about unshakable faith, uncompromising witness, and a life lived at full volume."

Matthew Rogers
Lead Pastor, First Christian Church,
Warsaw, Indiana

Till That Day Comes

"*Till That Day Comes* is the true story of a very special young lady and how, through the power of the Holy Spirit, she lived her last days with such poise, grace, and yes, sometimes humor. All who knew Sara were greatly moved. Her example deeply influenced my life and has led many to find the Lord she loved. You must read her story."

Dr. Earl Ferguson
Retired pastor of Community Christian Church at
Carillon, Plainfield, Illinois

Introduction

Long-faded significant memories often have a way of sticking with us, influencing who we are meant to become. The author and perfector of our faith also remembers working all things for the good of those who love Him. May we all glean what He desires to extend us in *Till That Day Comes* for such a time as this.

Many journey mates joined me in prayer regarding the details of this book, as well as God's timing for its release into the world. While some names and places remain the same, most names underwent changing for the sake of writing a compelling story for you. You will find great focus on our main character, Sara Schreck, for a good reason.

She worked out Jeremiah 29:11-13, *"For I know the plans I have for you,' declares the Lord, 'plans to prosper you and not to harm you, plans to give you hope and a future. Then you will call on me and come and pray to me, and I will listen to you. You will seek me and find me when you seek me with all your heart."* For all who seek, I hope God will use her journey to inspire you and clarify your purpose as well.

You are about to walk alongside some of the most precious ordinary people, whose faith drove them forward into the unknown and often into the consoling arms of a loving heavenly Father. They felt every feeling you may imagine, and their responses might just surprise you.

For those characters who lived alongside Sara in the early 1990s, you may notice the reality of unfinished conversations or your own longing for more time with Sara on the page. You are not alone. As I entrust *Till This Day Comes* into your eager hands, may you relish a few more moments with Sara, enjoy the rest of the story, and most of all, celebrate the evident grace of God in it all.

I write as a key witness to what you are about to dive into. I am Sara Schreck's oldest sister, also known as Dyane, throughout this story. In this light, I cannot contain my joy. We all welcome you and celebrate your presence with us as we reminisce. You'll watch our normal family days flow into days we gasped for breath. We stand on the shore of the past with you, vulnerable on the page without those beside us that once understood best. However, time cannot erase what God did. We are all connected still. As the church, may our heart chords tighten, both bound forever by Almighty God and our shared love for a teenaged girl named Sara Schreck.

Introduction

So, before the words draw you in, one thing remains. As you read *Till That Day Comes*—please allow yourself to rewind back in time, a time before cell phones, a time where phones were attached to walls with chords; no one heard of debit cards, or texting, streaming, or social media. A time when God spurred His people on to make His good news known in far simpler ways. Nevertheless, this story now spans eager generations.

I hope you will cherish this labor of love, eagerly share it, and know God inspired it all. May God bless you *Till That Day Comes*, when we all enjoy eternal fellowship together again.

Blessings by His grace, dear friends,
Kelly D. Schreck McManus

For it is by grace you have been saved, through faith—and this not from yourselves, it is the gift of God—not by works, so that no one can boast. For we are God's workmanship, created in Christ Jesus to do good works, which God prepared in advance for us to do.

Ephesians 2:8-10

Prologue

I came from a somewhat Christian family. My dad never really went to church. My mom did. From the time I was born to the time of age seven, we went to church, but my dad didn't like it. So, we went to another. I think the only reason he wanted to go there was to improve his status as a businessman. I don't think he wanted a relationship with God. As this was all happening, I was so confused about God and church. As I went, the kids already had their cliques, and I never felt a part of them. At about age nine, I was baptized, thinking it was the right thing to do since my sister was doing it with me. I really didn't know what being a Christian was. My father didn't help either. He was my only role model until my parents got divorced. When I saw him doing things, I also thought it was okay.

As the summers kept coming around, I was somewhat pressured into going to Christian camps with my cousin. The more I went to summer camp, though, the more I wanted to be a part of them. Little by little, I finally grasped what a Christian should be like. The only problem was, I had to apply it to my life...

Sara Schreck—Age fourteen

Chapter 1

Heart Of The Matter

Dyane hesitated. Her twenty-one-year-old heart beat fast, for she knew better than to offer her sister Sara advice at that moment. Instead, she clamped her lips together and fixed her eyes upon the closest evergreen tree outside her kitchen window. The painted wisps of white upon its branches offered a comforting snowy contrast to her warm knotty pine cabinets. Dyane welcomed the view and wrapped the front of her blue plaid shirt around her stomach. The draft from the windowpane bit and nipped at the rest of her exposed skin. She shivered. Swiping her wet palms over her jeans, she gazed upon her young husband Joseph sprawled upon the floral chair near their dining table. Her face grew warm. She spun her wedding ring between her fingertips. *He would know what to say if he wasn't… distracted,* Dyane thought. A metal bowl filled with half-eaten caramel corn called to her, reflecting the golden glow of an electric candle upon the sill behind Joseph's head. Outside, the vintage train depot's single string of rainbowed Christmas lights twinkled and swung with every wind gust. Their hazy colors melded with the neon movie rental sign, which hung in the depot window.

Against the blackening night, the Michigan snowfall intensified, and the kitchen grew cooler. Dyane rested her waist on the counter's edge across from Sara and debated whether or not to tackle washing her grandmother's encrusted casserole dish and turkey platter. She popped a piece of caramel corn into her mouth and traced the cream tile counter surface with a clean finger while she chewed. Dyane brightened.

"The dishes will wait—c'mon, it's time for some girl-talk," she stated.

As Joseph cackled at length in front of the television, Sara and Dyane slid across the slick wood planked flooring in their socks, down the hall, and towards the master bedroom filled with welcoming blankets.

As soon as Dyane closed her bedroom door, Sara exhaled, turned, and dropped herself backward in a dramatic free-fall onto Dyane's queen-sized bed. Upon landing, her chocolate curls sprung and whipped around her face. Many multi-colored throw pillows shook and enveloped Sara's head. Dyane laughed and tossed a rolling pillow back upon her youngest sister.

"You goofball!" Dyane teased.

While Sara wiggled about like a fish on the floor of a canoe, Dyane shook her head, knowing it was an impossible effort to calm her sister's giggles. Regardless, Dyane quite enjoyed the dramatic gestures of this blossoming teenaged woman before her eyes. Sara never left Dyane starving for a good laugh or encouragement. Reaching her hand out, she caught Dyane's and yanked her downward onto the rumpled heap of bedding surrounding her. The grapevine and floral wreath above Dyane's bed trembled against the wall. Neither noticed. Instead, both squealed with distress at their springy and less than graceful landings, which didn't knock a single throw pillow off the bouncing bedside. Dyane clenched at her waist with both palms and tipped over.

"I'm getting a cramp!" Dyane exclaimed.

"You gals okay in there?" Joseph asked from the other side of the bedroom door.

Dyane rolled her eyes and dropped her head into the

wrinkled covers.

"Yes—," she replied.

Her one-word answer—a non-invitation into their private conversation. Her heart leaped into her throat; she feared sacrificing any more time than she had to with her sister. Dyane rolled onto her back and covered her mouth, watching Sara hold her breath until the sound of Joseph's footsteps faded down the hallway. Then, Sara exhaled a hyper snort and laughed with such volume; spit spray landed upon Dyane as she hoisted her little sister upward by the hand. Sara shook her head, the pitch of her voice rose, and she pressed an available hand into her stomach. Dyane gasped with a squeal and swiped the spit off her neck with a shirttail.

"Ugh—I can't wait to get married," Sara announced.

Her eyes lifted to the ceiling as if she intended the words to become a plea-filled prayer.

At that, Dyane smiled, rolled her eyes again, and popped her sister in the arm with a nearby pillow.

"I bet you can't," she said.

Dyane grew quite familiar with Sara's desire to marry.

Even at the age of fifteen, Sara already knew the future she longed for. Laughing, Dyane straightened her comforter, and the sisters giggled until they swiped tears off their lower eyelids.

With dancing eyes, Dyane drew another breath and lowered herself onto the edge of her bed. She bit the inside of her lip, knowing she didn't want to ask the hard questions circling her mind but needed to. Crossing a leg underneath the other, Dyane's nail-bit fingers also fiddled with the dangling cross on a golden box chain falling below her neckline. She then found her courage to speak after slipping her fingertips underneath both her legs for warmth.

"I'm so glad you came up to visit and are willing to stay with us longer than you planned through New Year's Eve. So, now that I've got you for a few more days all to myself, you've got to spill it," she stated.

Dyane offered a calmer, less urgent, and softer voice than the one inside her head. She then slid nearer to Sara's side. Dyane's dachshund pushed the door open with her nose and hopped up onto the bed. Dyane stood and clicked the door shut before she returned. After welcoming her dog Kirby onto her lap, she then searched her sister's soft blue eyes.

They hadn't changed since the last time she visited her parents' Illinois home. Sara's weak grin met Dyane's, and she raised her teal green turtleneck collar up over her mouth. Appearing grateful they sat alone and unsure where to begin, Sara dropped her chin and pulled the fabric downward underneath it. Dyane fought the urge to reach out and hold her sister's hand. Instead, she smoothed and stroked her fingers over Kirby's black fur. The silence felt loud, and she felt conflicted. Dyane didn't rush to blurt out her opinions or her questions as she often did as a teen. However, she still felt tempted to. Both time and forgiveness laid to rest their childhood arguments, but up until that night, nothing removed Dyane's urge to fix others' problems. Regardless, in those quiet moments, the girls watched the silent snow continue its cascade on the other side of the windowpane and the collection within its corners. Sara then rubbed her palms on the surface of her jeans and proceeded to speak as if her own soul spilled and fell open.

"I don't feel right," she stated.

"What doesn't feel right, hun?" Dyane asked.

"Well, look at my skin; I'm all broken out. I'm feeling way more upset by things that never bothered me before. My

monthly cycle has stopped, and I'm worried." She pulled at
the front of her shirt.

"My clothes aren't fitting like they used to; I'm so uncomfortable that I've raided mom's closet for bigger sweat-
ers. I was a size eight, and now I'm a size twelve, Dyane—a
size twelve! That's like four sizes in four months! I feel like
everybody's looking at me now, especially when I'm eating. I'm so stressed out!" Sara stood, reached up, and then
stretched her curls outward from her head. "And look at my
hair; it's going crazy! It's so dark and frizzy! At least before,
the curls were tame. I can't stand it! And look at my face, right
here; you can even see the hair above my lip getting darker!"

Sara then stood, spun, and almost jogged to the adjoining
bathroom mirror to prove her point. Pressing her nose up to
her reflection, she stole a closer look, picked at her pimples,
and searched for anything else she had missed. Watchful of
her sister's bolt to the bathroom vanity, Dyane swiped the tip
of her nose from side to side in an effort to relieve its sting.
Then she clasped both hands upon her cheeks for warmth
and sighed.

From the moment her sister arrived for the brief Michigan visit, Dyane observed Sara. She watched her bright

smile diminish, and Dyane felt the creases between her own brows deepen. The changes overwhelmed her, and many unanswered questions still floated around Dyane's mind. She bit her thumb nail and thought, *Had Sara forgotten the internal beauty she still possessed? Does Sara feel ugly? Or adopted those ungracious thoughts about her round face or facial hair?* Oh, that hair, it seemed to Dyane as if the most detestable of all the changes in her little sister's eyes. As she continued to watch Sara prep for bedtime from the edge of her bed, Sara pursed her lips, then grabbed a wrinkled fabric hair tie off the bathroom counter. She swept a wide collection of her spiraled mane up and into a ponytail, allowing countless bent strands to remain untamed. Sara's eyes dropped, and she shook her head. That evening, the bathroom light exposed more than Dyane had expected to see. Sara's medium blonde, corkscrewed, shoulder-length hair darkened at least three shades since the last time they connected. By Sara's account, it grew coarser, frizzier, and an uncontrollable mass with every passing day. In spite of their hairdressing mom's advice, nothing calmed it. Dyane observed Sara, almost studied her. Sara's un-submissive wiry strands, while most obvious, also graced a body spinning out of control.

Sara returned with sagging shoulders to Dyane's bedside, her blinking began to quicken, and silent tears rolled down her pink rounded cheeks. They fell like a waterfall. Her blue eyes glimmered brighter as they watered and pleaded. Dyane reached for her sister's hand, squeezed it tight, and guided her to sit close. Dyane felt helpless. She struggled to find the perfect words to speak, but instead sandwiched her sister's left hand with her own and bit at a dry piece of skin on her lower lip. Feeling powerless to rescue Sara from such feelings, Dyane watched the black mascara collect underneath her sister's eyes. Sara swiped at both her lashes and a dripping nose with the tissue Dyane handed her. The image of Sara's face became blurry as Dyane listened, for she tried to see Sara's need from every available angle. It seemed to her that none of the baggy clothes Sara borrowed from their mother, the stylish outfits that remained hung in Sara's closet, or even Sara's well-applied makeup, masked the water retention, the puffiness, the acne, or the shame any longer. Dyane knew deep down, Sara must have hidden her figure so well at school behind oversized sweatshirts and a flirty, teasing personality that no one even questioned Sara's appearance. However, on this trip and in those honest moments, Sara allowed herself to embrace reality and stare at the pillow upon her lap, pick at its fuzz, and cry.

27

Emotional and naked before her big sister's eyes, Dyane reached out further, squeezed Sara's forearm, and held it tight. Sara then confessed through panicked sobs—

"I am eating oranges constantly, like at every meal. I'm even running up and down mom and dad's basement staircase a lot, like every day, but nothing's working."

After Sara revealed this to Dyane, Sara's eyebrows tilted, and another watery glance spoke of her troubles far more than words. She sniffed back the down-flow from her nose, found a tissue on the dresser nearby, and blew. Dyane waited. She waited for Sara, and she struggled through a silent prayer. So many thoughts pelted Dyane's mind. Sara's initial problem-solving ideas over the weight gain still alarmed her. *Did mom know? Why did she think eating oranges or running the staircase was the best option? What relentless thoughts prodded her mind each day!* As if Sara knew her sister's thoughts, she glanced at the ceiling before she cleared her throat and spoke—

"Dyane, I can't think about anything else. I had to do something to fix this," Sara explained.

Dyane's eyebrows tilted.

Heart of the Matter

"But Sara, this is just so... *intense!*" Dyane offered.

Dyane took mental notes of every description Sara made about her custom diet and exercise routine before concluding one thing—Sara's plan made perfect sense to Sara alone. After searching her fifteen-year-old sister's intense stare, Dyane knew attempting to convince her otherwise would prove impossible.

Sara's lengthy pause extended permission for Dyane to do the same. As her own head began to pound, she felt grateful for the conversational respite. Then, Sara's eyes brightened a bit.

"I am still cheerleading for basketball and running around with Alli, Heidi, and some girls from church, though. We're going to Matthew's Bible study on Sunday nights—which I love. I'm still in the student choir, and they have asked me to learn sign language with a lady from church so I can sign to some new songs for Youth Sunday," Sara said.

While she changed the subject and recalled the details of her social calendar, Dyane listened and took renewed comfort in her baby sister's smile.

"Also, Alice, Leigh, Lissa, and some other girls and I go

shopping, have sleepovers, and hang out whenever I'm not cheering at the basketball games."

"Oh Sara, that's awesome—you are staying busy!" Dyane exclaimed.

She exhaled another sigh of relief.

"What about your classes? Are they going alright?" Dyane asked. She still sought answers, anything to explain why her sister's appearance had changed. Dyane covered her yawn with her palm and struggled with her attentiveness. She then slid her fingers through a few short strands of her hair and began to twist them.

"Yea, English has been the most fun this year. I have this gorgeous blonde English teacher! He has a corny sense of humor, and I'm really trying to get him to go out with my computer teacher. This assignment he has us doing is kind of like a journal for the whole semester. Some days are so boring, ya know? Like what do I write other than, 'It's another boring day of high school, cheerleading practice, home, homework, and stuff?' Anyway, I'm having so much fun teasing him," Sara said.

Sara smiled. At her cue, Dyane sat up a little straighter

and questioned.

"Teasing him about what, Sara?"

Sara chuckled.

"Like, I write about the boys I like, and one time I wrote about a, um, a kiss," Sara stated.

She squinted, and her shoulders raised.

"What in the world, Sara? Are you *serious*?" Dyane blurted.

Sara giggled. Dyane raised her hands to her face and massaged her jaw. She pictured Sara's English teacher propped at his desk chair while grading a stack of stale journal entries until discovering Sara's in the pile. She imagined his squirm of discomfort. Sara's Cheshire grin had fun written all over it until Dyane dropped her hands into her lap with an expression that cooled Sara's smile down to an apprehensive smirk. She sat up a little straighter and pushed her shoulders back.

"Yea, well, maybe I shouldn't have told him, but it's just so hilarious! Maybe I've just got too much romance in me; seems like all I think about," she stated.

Sara's coy appearance alarmed Dyane and made her big sister blush. However, Dyane gave in to a snicker at Sara's way of expressing her frustration. Sara's classic defense of playing innocent didn't annoy Dyane as it used to. Instead, she covered her eyes with her hand. Sara loved to stir things up, as well as tease both of her sisters Dyane and Elizabeth, but between them, Dyane often played into the protective big sister role. She became frenzied whenever Sara brought up the subject of boys or crushes, and in this case—the muddied waters of Sara's romantic side grew muddier.

"Oh my word Sara, you're probably driving him crazy!" Dyane blurted. Sara rolled her own eyes, and her big sister saw her do it.

Dyane parted her lips, but nothing came out. Instead, her hesitation hung in the moment. *Should I press Sara with more questions?* She wondered and resisted yet again.

Chapter 2

Everything Changes

Underneath Dyane's exhale months later, she observed the frost spread across a section of her parents' sliding glass door. Its patterns held Dyane's attention and mesmerized her. On that frigid afternoon in 1993, Dyane encouraged the expanding flake-like etchings until a golden school bus stretched into the parking lot behind her parents' home. Brown leafless branches created just enough visual barrier to hinder her full view beyond the suburban lots chain link fence. Dyane, her mother Susan, stepfather Jim, and grandmother Irene all anticipated Sara's return home from school within minutes.

Dyane's taste buds drew her back to the kitchen, where they gathered. However, the kitchen snacks and conversations brought little peace of mind in the waiting. Dyane felt uneasy and nibbled the last of a chocolate chip cookie while Susan loaded the lunch plates into the dishwasher. Irene's fingertips tapped in perfect repetition, like a drum, upon the tile countertop. Dyane's mother's jaw clenched before her hand flew across the width of the island counter and cupped a palm over Irene's fingers.

"Mother, please *stop!*" She urged.

At once, Irene drew back on her seat and pulled her hand closer towards herself. She covered a wrinkled hand over the other in an effort to suppress her nervous habit. Dyane shifted on her own barstool. Irene stole a shy side glance at Dyane and shrugged her slumped shoulders with a sigh. Dyane raised her eyebrows and shared a reassuring toothless grin in return before clearing her drying throat.

As Susan turned toward the sink again, Jim approached her from behind and began a gentle rub with his hands at the base of her neck. Dyane observed her mother's head lower after a few gentle squeezes. Her mother's exhale at his touch said it all. Then, she reached her hand up, giving her husband's hand a peaceful pat.

Dyane twisted to glance at the wall clock where each slow click of the minute hand sounded like a time bomb. In addition to her own fear, as the oldest of the three sisters, she felt a strange mix of gratefulness and guilt. Sara hadn't known of Dyane's planned return home. The days they'd spent apart stretched into months since their last snowy Michigan visit, and she soon realized her brief return home to Illinois held the potential for strain. The agitation between her mom and grandma, while temporary, pained her. She meandered over to the family room's sliding door to identify a place to stand and scratched her head. Conflicted, Dyane felt pulled to return to the kitchen and retreat behind the kitchen counter to lean upon it. At the sight of the bus, however, she planted her feet and chose to remain near the sliding glass door instead.

From where Dyane stood, she saw a clear image of Sara hopping down steps while her curls bobbed up and down. She lugged an overfilled bookbag upon her shoulder, and a mittened hand clutched her purse close to her hip. In the far-off distance and through the glass barrier, Dyane surveyed the billows of air rising behind Sara's stride. Beyond the gnarly fence line brush, she found Sara's appearance more radiant than ever. Her shifting winter wear wrapped her from head to toe, and Dyane prized Sara's energy. In spite of her clothing hindrances, Sara swayed down the snow-dusted pavement and sidestepped the shoveled mounds. In the same vein, the motion of her glossed lips caught Dyane's attention, even though she struggled to make out the words. With their consistent movement and her wrinkling nose from time to time, Dyane reminisced. A makeshift stage and a turkey baster microphone danced into her mind, and the memory cheered her.

Dyane longed to surprise her sister and bring a smile to her face. She also desired the motivation to pop out from around a corner but instead considered the nausea she felt churning inside her stomach. Rather than draw attention, Dyane distanced herself from the door as soon as she saw Sara open the gate.

Susan's rapid unlatching of the back door before her daughter trudged across the patio caused their dog, Molly, to bark nearby. The frozen door required both hands to hoist it open. Sara stepped in, tapped her toes on the carpet to release a dusting of snow, and with one arm offered her mom a loose hug but firm kiss on the cheek.

"Hey, Mom," she said.

The landing thud of Sara's overstuffed book bag upon the wooden floor startled Dyane just like a jolt from a defibrillator.

"Hey, Jimmy! You're home early today," she stated.

Everything Changes

Her stepfather's eyes brightened, and he stepped forward for a side hug.

"Yep," he said.

His head nodded, and his mouth straightened into a tight line.

Sara didn't hesitate; hugging her grandma allowed her to nuzzle her cold nose into Irene's collar. Irene wiggled and offered Sara the satisfaction of a little squeal. Obvious and dramatic Sara shook her body.

"Man, it's cold out there!"

Dyane witnessed her sister's boisterous entry and failed to recall Sara ever coming through a door in silence. In Dyane's opinion, her baby sister always made quite a spectacular entrance. Yet, on this dreary day, the greetings touched her, and their radiance filled her with comfort. This gentle wave of compassion for her family reminded Dyane why she drove in from Michigan. Sara grabbed at her outer layers, appearing anxious to peel off the rest and drop them to the ground next to her boots and mittens. A sight to behold from where she stood, Dyane still admired Sara's beauty in spite of the additional pounds she carried, and her reddened cheeks made her blue eyes glow all the more. The joy made

Dyane's insides quiver. As she laid eyes upon Sara again—she felt a maternal love for her sister. This intensity seemed stronger than any other time she recalled, and Dyane's eyes drank Sara in one sip at a time.

She sucked in her breath when Sara's sight caught her own; Dyane emerged from the shadowed background. Sara raised her shoulders and ran towards her. Dyane welcomed her approaching grin, teenaged squeals, and tight hugs. She never thought she'd tire of them. Dyane pulled away only to search her sister's elated face for a moment. Unobvious during their previous visit, she noticed Sara's sea-blue eyes dimmed to the palest shade of cornflower blue. Holding fast, they rocked each other from side to side.

Susan, Jim, and Irene advanced slow and easy towards them, showing great respect for their moment. They all clustered close together smiling, and while they wove through small talk, they warmed each other with more than words. Susan and Jim's hands clasped together. Dyane's heart ached and participated in the surreal event as if in slow motion. In spite of the comfort the moments provided, her stomach free fell as soon as Susan stopped talking. Studying Sara's eyes, her mother waited for them to connect with her own. Dyane's lungs filled tight; remembering to breathe was difficult.

Everything Changes

Susan wanted Sara's attention, and Dyane gave it to her. She also reached sideways for Sara's hand while their mother's lips quivered. Susan's attempt to keep herself from crying had failed.

"What? What is it?" Sara questioned.

Her forehead rippled, and her free hand pressed the top of her chest.

"Mom?" Sara questioned.

She dropped Dyane's palm and shifted closer to her mother before their own hands clasped into tight knots. Dyane held a hazy awareness of her fingers spinning the wedding ring below her knuckle in circles. Jim cleared his throat, and Susan cleared her own as well before speaking. She gazed at Sara, then spoke nine simple words which encapsulated all they knew so far.

"Sar—the call came in from the doctor's office. Your adrenal gland has become an eight-inch tumor," Susan said.

In the wake of their mother's trailing words, Jim, Irene, and Dyane all entwined their arms, pressed their fingertips upon each other's shoulders and waists, and created a partial huddle. Dyane refused to let go of anyone and allowed her nose to drip while the tears fell. Their shoulders shook, off rhythm, while their voices melded into a grievous tone. Their grandmother, Irene, sought Sara's response with her eyes while appearing grey, pasty, and queasy. The weakness in Dyane's legs forced her to balance upon the one who stood beside her. She felt thankful for her grandmother's fragile support, all to avoid a near-collapse to the wooden floor. Within those moments, Jim's nose began to flair, and his lips quivered. Irene covered her mouth, and Dyane's pulse raced. Sara covered her face and buried herself into her mother's neck, wailing and screaming like a young child—

"Will I die? I don't want to die... Mom, *I don't want to die!*"

***

The lonely days apart turned into weeks of vibrant winter sunrises and lavender brushed sunsets. In spite of their beauty, their family's state of mind didn't leave room for appreciation. Nothing else seemed to matter more than closing the miles between them all and helping Sara get well again. Dyane returned to her quaint Michigan home and waited. However, her household routine failed to distract her. She daydreamed often at her desk while preparing her first and second-grade Sunday School class lessons. The heart-stenciled walls encircled her, and she grew quieter. Dyane felt limited in her travel provisions. She and Joseph shared one car plus Joseph's $250.00, a week youth minister's salary. Regardless of her sparse circumstances, each day, she tucked her bedding in, washed her face, picked up her Bible, fed the dog, and pushed the normal button upon her washing machine. The routine mattered, as did the moments she cared about the church kids and their families with Joseph. She felt lost at times, but their distraction brought the stress relief she needed to rise above so many unknowns.

One morning, while Dyane stared out the window with hands bound in soapsuds, her kitchen phone clamored. Unable to find a nearby towel, she flicked the bubbles onto her wooden floor and lunged across the counter to catch the receiver.

"Hey honey, it's me; I've got some news for you," Susan greeted.

"Oh, hey, Mom! Oh my goodness—hold on a sec, let me get a pad of paper," Dyane stated.

"No problem, honey," Susan replied.

While Susan waited on a silent line, an increase of adrenaline heated Dyane's face the longer she rummaged through a nearby junk drawer. Clicking pen after pen, she swirled them on paper with little success.

"Ugh, where's a working pen? Got it! Alrighty, I'm ready, Mom," Dyane stated.

Susan exhaled into the mouthpiece to ready herself.

"Well, Sara's doctor has recommended a surgeon out of Rush Presbyterian Hospital in Chicago," Susan stated.

Dyane heard another loud sigh through the earpiece.

"Gosh, Mom, the traffic alone back and forth from Chicago will exhaust both you *and* Grandma!" Dyane exclaimed.

"We'll figure it out; I know Dyane, it's not ideal, but what else can we do?" Susan questioned.

At the strain in each other's voices, Dyane began to run her fingers through her hair.

"I'm sorry, I'm just worried, I guess. I wish I were there, Mom," Dyane said. "Thanks for this; please tell Sara I love her. And please tell Grandma too."

Everything Changes

After their goodbyes, Dyane circled the date upon her calendar and felt a wave of problematic tension encompass her body. She rubbed her neck hard before sinking into the overstuffed floral chair and pulled a folded afghan up to her chin. She didn't feel guilty. At the moment, her body, her mind, her emotions all hungered for rest. Alone and in the silence of her home above the oak furniture store, her eyes filled again. This time, not with relief, as much as helplessness. She felt guilty. With one hand, Dyane massaged the base of her neck again, and she began to feel the room spin. She knew stopping the news of Sara's tumor and her upcoming surgery to family, neighbors, friends, and churches all over the United States—impossible. She wanted to get off the dizzying ride. Dyane dropped her head into her hands and sobbed like a baby. She didn't know how to choose joy in the midst of her pain. At the moment, she wanted to flee her little town wafting of fried, glazed donuts, its rattle of trains passing the quaint depot, its picturesque furniture store with its covered porch, their church family and set off for Chicago.

Chapter 3

A Family Like Yours

Time seemed to crawl until Dyane's return to Illinois, but the black circled date upon her calendar nevertheless arrived. The high-rises proclaimed a towering welcome towards Sara's family as they caravanned back into the city. Some extended family members, as well as herself, failed to question if the hospital had a policy on the limit of visitors. Doubtful, they all stopped for a guest pass; Dyane felt jumpy and looked at the room entrance often. She knew if they all tried to crowd into Sara's pre-op room on surgery day, more than one rule might break. In a rebellious fashion, they as well as close friends, continued their trickle into Sara's sterile hospital room. Anne, Allen, Nicole, and Brittany, the youngest cousins, gathered at Sara's bedside, enthralled by the buttons, gears, and tubes. Everyone else clumped around the room, appearing oblivious before Sara's roll down to surgery. The children's miniature voices whispered to their mothers, asking about the long lines streaming from Sara's arms to the pole looming behind them. Sara smiled and assured her Aunt Marie, Uncle Thomas, Aunt Judy, and Uncle Allen that she didn't mind the expectant and curious questions from their children. Sara explained everything she thought of, taking care to point to each route from the fluid bag to the IV line entering the top of her hand. The bulging tape covered the spot where it supplied the antibiotics before her surgery. Every child paid attention, following her finger with their eyes. They oohed and aahed, marveling at Sara's knowledge and understanding.

Dyane slid back the blue dividing curtain, rolling it along its track to create more space. She swiped her forehead with a napkin from her purse and shoved a piece of peppermint gum into her mouth. Her stomach churned, and she chewed faster, hoping to silence the growling with its sweet minty flavor. Dyane felt lightheaded and eyed Sara's Styrofoam cup filled with melting ice chips.

Rather than her family's initial somber appearance, Dyane noticed visible changes since the tumor announcement. It appeared the delays to Sara's surgery allowed their family time to process and reflect. Sprinkled throughout the patient room, they waited with Sara. Instead of gloom, a brighter optimism, laughter, and conversation filled the air. Much had transpired, and Susan didn't hesitate to smooth out Sara's tan blankets or massage Sara's legs underneath.

"Hey, kids, the nurse needs to check Sara's blood pressure," Jim said.

The littles' parents drew them back, and he lifted his wife by the hand from the bedside. He kissed Susan on the top of the head and pulled her close. While he watched the nurses come and go, Susan turned up her hearing-aides with the twist of a fingertip.

Sara laughed in response to something Leah said, and as the last nurse left, the conversations multiplied. Outbursts of laughter flowed out of Sara's room and into the hallway. No one admitted to the possibility their crowd broke the rules. However, Dyane shook her head at Joseph for speaking with their brother-in-law, Neil, in a regular-toned voice. Regardless of her caution, no one came barreling in from the nurse's station. So, she proceeded to take a chance of her own, letting go of some felt need to control both their situation and her husband. Her stepfather Jim heard her deep exhale and met her gaze with a gentle grin. Once Dyane heard her mother Susan speaking above a loud whisper, the intense self-conscious worries plaguing the pit of her stomach dwindled a bit more. The room reverberated, and Dyane held her side after a lengthy giggle. Appearing pleased, Sara glanced around at the crowd surrounding her bed. Dyane felt grateful for these moments and believed the calming and healing salve of to-getherness softened Sara's expression. She felt glad, glad that not one shadow of fear appeared to veil Sara's glowing face that morning. Dyane felt encouraged and readied her-self to face whatever came—together.

"Okay, Sara. We are about ready for you. Do you need anything else?" a nurse asked.

"Umm," Sara hesitated.

The nurse's yellow gauze cap puffed wide and low upon the crown of her head, and her bright pink shirt shown of unrecognizable characters to Dyane. She noticed the nurse's perky personality and witnessed it draw Sara's attention. As Dyane hung onto the silence for Sara's answer, the nurse twisted the almost emptied bag, examined the IV tubes, and pressed buttons on the infusion pump. Dyane's breaths slowed with every passing second and held them longer and longer. Then, just before stepping out into the hallway again, she placed her hand upon Sara's shoulder. "So, what else can

I get you?"

Dyane breathed a sudden sigh of relief.

"Nothing, thanks; I think I'm good," Sara stated.

"Okay, we'll be back for you real soon," said the nurse.

Dyane overheard their grandma Irene's voice shake and muffle out a response to the nurse's announcement.

"Oh, no—" she said.

Irene brought a fist up to her mouth. She then widened her watering eyes as she leaned into the oversized picture window's sill. Dyane's grandfather dropped his head, received his wife's hand, and stifled his own tears until his shoulders shook.

"Hey, everyone. Hey, let's go ahead and form a circle around Sara's bed as best as we can right now, and let's pray for her," their youth pastor Matthew suggested.

Sara tilted her chin upward. Her smiling eyes fixed upon him, and she nodded. The group voiced their prayers after trembling hands took hold of the clammy ones next to them. Dyane's nose tingled, and she felt as if she stood in someone else's shoes. One by one, their voices rose in turn. At Dyane's moment to pray, she consented in agreement with the silent thoughts flowing from her heart—"God, please help— yes, *please help Sara*. She's yours, so loved, so treasured. Please, Father, have mercy upon her and help her through this surgery. Please, guide the surgeons, give them wisdom, and please, give us all more strength, endurance, and grace through this. In Jesus' name, Amen."

After placing more dependence upon God and filling with thankfulness, Dyane let the hands that grasped her own, drop. She welcomed the new peaceful feeling inside her heart and the lightness that leaning on Him brought. Dyane often prayed over her meals and before bed. Offering a silent prayer during a church service or after reading her Bible became familiar to her also. However, on this day, something new began to happen in the room where they gathered around Sara. She listened to the people she loved pray aloud, and something awoke and stirred within her. She even felt the heaviness in her chest rise for a moment.

Dyane stood in a bent line to see Sara before she left the room. Before she knew it, one simple thought led to contemplation, which then overtook her mind and tempted her to panic. Her pulse quickened. *I don't know which is worse, carrying a large tumor around in your body or waiting to be cut open to take it out.* Dyane sucked in a deep breath and shut her eyes. Her neck began to perspire. It took every effort to manage more thoughts like it and barricade their flow into her mind. She dared not state anything to Joseph and pressed her tongue to the roof of her mouth. When Dyane's turn in line came, she bent toward the reclined hospital bed; her hand smoothed back Sara's falling ringlets, and she brushed a kiss across Sara's forehead. Dyane bent around the vining tubes and the wires that branched from her body, all in an awkward effort to hug her sister with care.

"I love you, and I'll see you after surgery," she said.

Behind those tightening words within her throat, a striking feeling of dependence upon God's mercy and desire for forgiveness rushed through Dyane's mind and shouted—*I'm so sorry sis, that I ever treated you with coldness and anger. I should have forgiven you more. I'm sorry I didn't set a better example for you. I'd rather be the one on the gurney waiting to roll to surgery. I do want to protect you as your big sister, I do—but can't, I am so weak. I love you more than I'm able to say!* Dyane swiped at her eyes with the back of her hand as she stepped toward the crowd-filled doorway.

Till That Day Comes

Standing in the wings of Sara's pre-op room, the nurses also waited, clothed not just in their bold green, blue, pink, and pale yellow, child-friendly patterned shirts, but with patience as each kiss and hug traveled around the room. They stood at length, quietly staring, and fixed their sights on the group before them with more than one widened eye. Although Dyane didn't feel judged or rushed, she hoped their appearance spoke what she remembered one person stating in the past—*You know, I've never met a family like yours.* Her lips curved as she remembered. Then, just before the outflow toward the elevators, every adult that caught a nurse's gaze smiled.

"Thank you," one after another said to the nurses. "Truly, thank you—," said another as they took their exits. Dyane also thanked them, grateful for their care for her sister as well as her family.

The time had come for Sara to roll out of the room upon her squeaking bed and pass through the swinging doors. Dyane stole one last glance behind her while moving farther away from the exit. The creases between Dyane's eyes grew deeper, and she folded her arms across her chest, offering herself a hug. Dyane's husband, Joseph, must have noticed her hands gliding over the surface of her arms because he didn't hesitate to reach out. His right arm swept around her waist, and he strolled beside Dyane down the art-filled corridor following their family and friends. With gentleness and care, he guided her closer toward his side. In those moments, regardless of any pressing marital conflict they may have shared on the way into the city that morning, Dyane sighed. She felt grateful for his presence, and Joseph's warm and loving hands touching her gave her goosebumps. It also gave her strength. It renewed her love for him. She felt a momentary heartache for her young marriage, all the changes, and uttered a silent prayer. They needed God's help. With every step, the tension between her shoulder blades melted.

Their crowd descended as one mass, down the multiple floors into the confines of a family waiting area. A light blue vinyl couch angled around the backside of the room and faced the television. Some pulled games and books out of their totes to keep the children busy but most clustered around the room chatting. Dyane watched the shrinking expanse offer less room for another person to sit. However, as her father Gerald arrived, with the help of some sitting next to her, she shifted her body a few more inches to her left and carved out a place for him to wedge himself onto the seat. His gripping hand rested upon Dyane's shoulder and pushed into it for balance. As always, she braced herself. Her heart beat faster and her green eyes watered under the pain of his grasp. *Why, why does he do that? Let go, hurry, please*—even without the insensitive clamp of his hand, she sensed his tension. Still, she empathized with him and the unfamiliar situation he strolled into. He said little and sat stiff with his bulky arm around her shoulders. Everyone in Dyane's family stood and sat a little straighter when Gerald had entered the room. While awkward, their gracious small talk with him seemed to offer only a temporary remedy to a bulging vein on his neck. Dyane, for one, felt glad for Sara's sake; he showed up. Dyane knew it didn't take much for her father to affirm his negative family reputation by showing up late and ignoring a few in the room. However, as she expected, his presence that day added another emotional burden. At that moment, under the pressure of his muscular arm, Dyane knew he might initiate something none of them had the courage to stop. She rubbed her temples with her fingers—pressure built behind Dyane's eyes and became a full-blown headache.

While disappointment in his behavior grew over the years—Dyane wondered if some in her family still struggled to forgive him as she once had. Her grandfather avoided making eye contact with him. Her mother and Jim sat at a distance. Her Uncle Thomas extended his hand like an olive branch every time they reunited, but it offered little resolution to a long history of family conflict. They knew him. Dyane wondered if any unspoken words or unforgiveness remained between them. Dyane sighed and closed her eyes, remembering the reasons for some of the division. She wondered if God knew about the burden her father's presence created for everyone. It seemed almost trivial compared to Sara's surgery but regardless, she needed to do something with her increasing anxiety. Dyane found it difficult to take a deep breath and found her shallow breathing quickening instead. She shut her eyes and tried to straighten her spine, but her ribs readily bent toward her stomach soon after. Dyane exhaled another silent prayer, feeling crushed in every way and knowing she needed an intervention beyond herself.

In spite of the strain, Gerald's familiar scent did comfort Dyane's soul somehow, reminding her of happier days. He smelled as clean as always, with the right balance of aftershave and cologne. She especially welcomed the spicy aroma in lieu of the recycled and stale hospital air. Each one of his sun-bleached hair strands remained in its place. His clothes hung on his tan, fit body with crispness—as if worn right from the dry cleaners. Dyane observed her young father's arm covered in glistening blonde hair and a gold-crowned watch hugging his wrist. It ticked away the hours of Sara's surgery, deepening her grief. His left hand stroked down his chin and then his neck. When Dyane glanced at him, she didn't see joy; she saw regret. Not only did she see the regret, she saw longing, frustration, and emptiness. Furthermore, in her daughter-like observation, his flexing neck muscle gave her clues into his tension. In reality, Dyane knew he lacked complete control over where he sat at the moment, over who operated on his baby girl, or over who sat with him. He appeared tired of hearing about God and joining in on everyone's hope-filled prayers, yet he seemed determined over one thing—to step into the decision-making role over the medical protocol for Sara. Dyane knew him as a man of action, and Susan spoke of it also. She also saw it in his crazed eyes as he stood. He paced in front of a lengthy picture window overlooking the skyline, appearing determined to make something happen. As the day grew longer, it became clearer to Dyane he might try to stir up trouble.

The surgeon's stride into the waiting room that afternoon made them all lift taller upon their seats again. Dyane's family rose as he entered. She shifted from one foot to the other, processing his words, and mulled over them long after he left the room. He described the adrenal tumor as a water balloon eight inches round, but Dyane's stomach dropped to her feet at the words *lesions* and *liver*. She wondered and worried in silence while he spoke—*should we take comfort that he took out every lesion on the surface of her liver or the ones in plain sight?* Dyane bit at another nail. *Were there any he couldn't see?* At the doctor's exit, the air seemed to thicken as her father followed him out through the swinging doors. After everyone else scooped up their bags, they all slunk out of the surgical waiting room in silence.

Hours later, Dyane and her mother tiptoed into the darkened Intensive Care Unit's recovery room. Even in the dim grey lighting, Dyane observed Susan swipe at her eyes upon first sight of Sara lying in bed. This evidence of her mother's love and relief comforted Dyane. It showed her what faith looks like in unexpected suffering, and the return of her mother's soft grin reflected her joy in the midst of it. Susan took a deep breath. She then leaned over the armrest and swept back the frizzed wayward ringlets upon her youngest daughter's forehead. Dyane stood opposite her mother, shivered with a chill, and covered her sister's shoulders a bit more. Sara's pale face lay still but restful under the sparse fluorescent lamp, and its light made the dark shadows of the room settle deeper into the corners behind them. Their mother's words released a song that drew Sara out from the place where her spirit rested. *"Sara, Saaara..." Susan called.*

While Dyane observed her mom caress Sara's temple and cheek ever so softly, she considered her mother's strength and heart's ache as she waited for Sara's eyes to open. She wondered if her mom ever feared this, one of her own children recovering from a major surgery like this one. The thought made Dyane's insides grieve, and she felt helpless, yet again. She despised these new emotions; Dyane never knew what to do with them once they overtook her, and she dabbed at the corners of her lids with a sleeve. However, in spite of those dismal feelings, something humorous swirled around in Dyane's memory—not long before the surgery, Sara declared a grim nickname for her tumor—*Hannah from hell.* Dyane contrasted Sara's disgust for carrying the tumor with her own hope of carrying a child one day. Sara carried grief. Dyane's future dream of motherhood carried elation. She fretted over Sara's awakening to her new scar, a reminder of the wicked tumor that once took up residence within her. At that moment, Dyane considered the comparisons while she looked upon her still sister, just lying there. Yet, she knew the one on Sara's side, and no one else fought like Sara. Once she woke, Dyane believed God for the victory in Sara's hard-fought fight.

Two by two, loved ones stepped into the recovery room. Sara's eyes drooped, and she struggled to lift them for more than a few seconds. Every adult trickled in to bless her with their presence and offer a soothing word. However, as their Aunt Judy and Uncle Allen entered her room, they set a peculiar unwrapped gift by Sara's side. Her gaze fell upon its wiry white hair, and she shifted the gift with a slow movement of her tube-tangled hand. Frizz-covered puppy dog ears and glistening black eyes both peeked back at Sara from below oversized eyebrows.

"His name is Putter Paws," her aunt announced.

His placement and repositioning upon Sara's chest caused more than one snicker to all who filed in afterward. Putter Paws, an unattractive creature, appeared as if squeezed too much already. The shabby thing lifted Sara's spirits higher, and she welcomed the distraction. Sara raised his white furry brow with her finger, peeked underneath at his beady eyes, and swallowed to clear her scratched throat. She spoke in a whisper while clutching him as tight as her weak arms allowed.

"He's so—cute," she said.

"You hold him tight when you have to cough," Aunt Judy replied.

Because of their heart-melting generosity, this fluffy varmint found its purpose and a new friend. He stood at attention upon Sara's chest in the ICU that day—waiting for the work entrusted to him.

***

Houseguests and a parade of visitors came and often went from the Gillespie house over the weeks that followed Sara's surgery. Susan and Jim dug themselves into parenting their two remaining teenaged girls at home, managing their high school demands, screening phone calls, making medical appointments, paying bills, attending physician meetings, negotiating insurance payments, upholding household responsibilities, coordinating three work schedules, and overseeing the additional troubles of each day. On the evening before Sara's tumor test results came back, their mutual exhaustion began to take its toll.

A Family Like Yours

"Thank you, honey; we appreciate you staying back," Susan stated. "We need some time alone."

Dyane agreed and welcomed her responsibility. Early the next morning, the extra bodies sprinkled around their family room didn't stir when they twisted the front door lock behind them. Jim and Susan made their escape down the steps and held hands towards the car. Dyane knew her parents needed time with Sara by themselves during their scheduled visit to the ICU, but it didn't erase her longing to crawl into the car and go with them.

Hours later, some out-of-town family members rose from their beds and perched upon the kitchen stools to snack on potato chips, cereal, and leftover brownies from the tray brought the day before. Some people remained folded inside fleece blankets, watching television, and flipped through magazines curled up on the couch. Little cousins hopped up the stairs from grandma Irene's basement apartment and continued toward the playroom upstairs. Dyane brushed a hand down her face, feeling intimidated by the preparations before her. She tried busying herself by picking up clutter on the counter and washing the encrusted pile of dishes everyone nestled inside the wet kitchen sink. Mail stashed underneath the phone toppled, and shoes multiplied to the left of the front door. Dyane felt her breaths quickening, and she fought the temptation to release a dam of tears. It all overwhelmed her. Her heart beat faster at the thought of tackling every task alone. Dyane massaged the base of her neck. Her thoughts spun as she didn't know where to start. Every household chore lagged behind, as did the many new responsibilities her parents now managed. Dyane caught someone out of the corner of her eye rushing across the upstairs hallway—attempting to sneak into the bathroom for a hot shower. Regardless of the extra work it meant for her, she felt very aware of her need to step up, as did her Aunt Judy and Grandma busy in the lower level kitchen. While appearing focused on the tasks, their countenances as well as their words, both modeled soft gratefulness to those around them. Gratefulness in this situation didn't come easy to Dyane, but it motivated her to serve alongside them anyway. In truth, she needed to welcome the responsibility as the first married cousin of the bunch. This thought caused her to stand up straighter. She loved the family chaos, and she didn't want to miss any of it.

After swishing the dishes under the streaming faucet, she glanced at the clock and wondered what the surgeon meant by *lesions* when he spoke to them all after the surgery. At that moment, she jumped within her skin at the shrilling phone ring, which caught her off guard. She splashed the sponge brush into the mirky sink water and seized the phone's handle with a damp hand. Those nearby drew closer and waited as Dyane listened to her stepdad Jim's weary voice.

"Hey Dy, we got up to the hospital alright and asked the pediatric nurse when we would be hearing from the doctor. We waited a bit, and after his return phone call came into the nurse's station, we were told…" He stopped mid-sentence to clear his throat, "It's cancer."

Dyane's stomach dropped, and so did a flow of warm tears upon her face. Each one soon felt cool on her warming cheeks. Her eyes blurred, and without a tissue handy, her fingertips brushed the corners of her eyes. Her nose began to run, and she sniffed a few times—all the while speechless. Dyane didn't know what to do or say. In those slow-moving moments, she contemplated. *Why can't I stop crying? Is it horror? Is it grief? Is it gratefulness for a definitive answer?* Yes, the tears covered all those things and much more. The diagnosis seared into her mind—Adrenal Cortical Carcinoma. As if those long words didn't frighten her enough, Dyane learned the doctors knew of only one known person, living in the Dominican Republic, who shared the same form of cancer. Dyane felt herself deflate, melt in fact, but Jim's comforting voice lured her thoughts back to reality.

"The options Sara has—are to go to Mayo Clinic or do chemotherapy with a liver transplant."

***

The calendar read February 23rd, another typical Chicago day, where the sky and its surroundings dressed themselves in flat shades of grays and browns. The blast of Windy City weather stung Sara's face once she emerged beyond the hospital corridor threshold. The wheels of her chair spun into the darkened parking garage lit by amber lights. Sara held her scarf up to her face and covered her nose with it to filter out the chill and car exhaust. During her trek home, amongst the brick and steel high-rises, the heavy traffic intensified unspoken anxiety within the car. Sara wiggled and squirmed underneath her blanket in the back seat. It seemed no new sitting angle gave her comfort or relief. Sara's upright position put an increasing strain on her curving incision, pulling at it from every direction. She grimaced, pushing steamy pants of air out through her lips. Every attempt to adjust and console herself amidst the urgent stabbing pain failed. Sara stretched both legs upon the cloth seat next to her and leaned backward against a pillow, preparing for the forty-minute car ride home. She covered her head and laid it upon Elizabeth's shoulder. Welcoming it, Elizabeth nuzzled herself closer and pulled the falling blanket over Sara's lap.

Minutes passed by, feeling like hours with every jarring bump in the road and through stop-and-go Chicago rush-hour traffic. Sara opened her eyes again to stare out the window, trying to distract herself from the gasping stabs of discomfort. Nearby car fumes poured into the cracked windows while their parents' cigarette smoke plumed upward and escaped between the glass and doorframe. Sara held her breath for as long as possible while engulfed in the pungent odor. Then, in quiet desperation for cleaner air, she brought the blanket up to her nostrils again and breathed through the tight woven fibers for the rest of her shaky ride home.

Upon their arrival, Sara approached the front door at a snail's pace while Dyane looked on. Sara closed her eyes often. Dyane's empathy, as well as the pain, became almost too much to bear. *Sister, yes, I am in great pain. I am feeling motion sick. I'm feeling nauseated by the secondhand smoke, and every step is so hard to take! Keep going, Sara, keep going; you're almost inside!* She held the doorframe and hoisted her foot up and onto the first step, hunched over like a fragile elderly woman, allowing herself guidance inside the foyer. On each side of her, the men braced Sara's elbows underneath. They then upheld and led her to the reclining chair set up for the night. The ladies bustled about, took coats, helped untie and removed Sara's tennis shoes, carried her overstuffed bags upstairs, and set up her seat with multiple pillows and blankets. After her descent upon the seat cushion in the slowest of motions, she gripped the nearest arms, then Sara smiled. She exhaled and welcomed the blanket her mom tucked around her legs. The women also made make-shift beds by draping blankets upon the sectional couch for Dyane and her younger sister Elizabeth. Observing their bedding stretched around the room, Dyane let out another slow breath of her own, appearing helpless as she stood nearby.

Their meager efforts seemed almost childlike. It appeared as if a campout or sleepover theme for the evening—minus the popcorn or the movie. Sara knew her pain medications invoked deep sleep and felt relieved for her sisters as they made preparations to awaken often through the night and help her. They seemed eager to help and did not mind assisting her treks to the bathroom or bedding readjustments. Once Sara settled in, she hoped to give her mom a full night's rest.

A Family Like Yours

After ringing the doorbell midevening, Sara prepared for her father Gerald, who stood upon the snowy front porch. Sara observed Dyane bite at her lip as he entered the custom home he built. He pounded the snow off of his dress shoes and rubbed his hands with speed over his lightweight black jacket and designer slacks. Polite, welcoming handshakes greeted him but also reminded Sara that Jim now lived there. At once, warmth and perspiration traveled through her body, feeling guilt over her distraction rather than her brightening gratefulness over his coming. She tried to focus and waved from her seat. She watched her dad Gerald wave back and glanced around the room. Sara wondered if he felt uncomfortable around the family he chose to leave behind.

"You all are the best things that ever happened to me," Sara remembered him confessing to her over a disappearing glass of vodka.

Tentative steps brought him through the familiar tiled hallway, and then his eyes fixed upon her once energetic body. Reclining on the couch, Sara sat colorless, covered in her blanket. Yet, she still offered a half-grin to her father. To bide the time of healing, a side table held half-empty cups, tissues, and a messy stack of reading material. Gerald smiled at her with loving sensitivity, moved her coughing buddy

Putter Paws, and sat down. Everyone came and went from the room, observing both of them facing each other with soft grins and held hands. They littered the silence with pretty small talk. As the night drew later, their conversation drained her. She felt poured out and emptier than the half-filled glass of water beside her chair. Dyane sat nearby to offer a comment or two to fill in the gaps as Sara's deflated strength became more obvious. She felt grateful for that. The welcome respite lasted long enough for her to grasp a few moments between sharp pains to plant intentional seeds about God. His numb nods met her unexpected words, for he didn't appear to know what to say and sat silent. Sara yawned more than once, and her eyes weighed heavy.

Not long after, when her words ran thin, their father released his grasp and laid Sara's pale hand upon the tan crocheted blanket with a pat. He rose to smooth out his thin dress pants. After he turned and leaned over to kiss her goodbye—she paused, lifted her head, and searched his gaze. Sara caught the growing glimpse of fear in his hazel eyes. He appeared he didn't want to leave. His lips tightened, and his words faded just before he hugged them. He then made his way to the front door, spun the handle, and allowed another arctic blast into the foyer. He shivered and waved, appearing antsy to keep moving. Sara raised her heavy hand. Dyane rose from her seat to say goodbye and shut the door, but the wind slammed the glass door closed instead. Sara felt her heart ache as Dyane stood watching him. Sara imagined his grief as Dyane cracked the storm door, and she heard her sister call out to him before closing it again.

"Bye, Dad—," Dyane said.

Chapter 4

Always On My Mind

The snow upon the front porch crunched underneath Gerald's leather loafers. His head both ached and pounded. The heat upon his forehead propelled itself over his clenched jaw and down his neck. The bitter cold almost felt good to him; the sting numbed the pain and angst within his chest. He scrambled to escape the foyer. Jim and Susan's welcome into the home he built disgusted him. Their warm greetings seared into his thoughts. *They don't deserve this house. They didn't pay for it. They didn't have to grovel or convince their father that investing in this home would benefit him and his mother in the summer months. He knew I couldn't afford it without his help. And now, here, my ex-wife and her husband are acting like I'm the guest. Give me a break!*

He shook inside, sucked in quick, shallow breaths, and began to feel lightheaded. His hands stung. Gerald forgot his leather gloves in the front seat of the car but didn't bother stuffing them into his pockets for warmth. The distraction felt good. He heard his eldest daughter's voice behind him, but it muffled once it reached the increasing drumbeat inside his head. He resisted turning and responding to her. Justified, he remembered—*she always ignored my instructions as a child or cried to her mother when I'd make her obey me. She never said hello when I'd walk in the door after a long day but sat in front of the television. Why did I even bother trying to give them so much? Airplanes, boats, cars, clothes, everything new—they didn't need anything, and she still avoided me. Now, here she is, married and grown-up—saying goodbye? Not thanks for coming from Arizona, Dad. Not how are you doing, Dad? Not I'll miss you, Dad.*

He had to keep moving, but after stepping away from the front porch, he bent. Gerald attempted to catch a deep enough breath to continue. He rubbed his hands over his thighs and hated himself for leaving Sara so soon, hated himself for living in Arizona, and hated himself for not protecting his baby girl from cancer. Bearing the regrets grew heavier—he never felt so worthless or inept. He labored to stop his eyes from glazing over, thickening in the freezing temperature, and blurring. *I have to get to the car;* he thought as he fished for his keys in his pocket. He fumbled to find the right one in the dark, swiped at his eyes, and relied upon the glow of the exterior garage lights to guide him.

After he started the rental car, Gerald noticed Dyane still watched him, this time from the front bay window. His regret resurfaced, and his chin dropped and swayed. *I'm sorry I didn't say goodbye, honey.* At the thought of his neglect, he felt repulsed. He seized the steering wheel and shook it. Groaning, he then buried his face within his freezing hands. The sobs both overwhelmed and shamed him. Gerald longed to flee the driveway he installed over a decade beforehand, but the tears forced him to stay put.

Once calmed, Gerald depended upon his memory and the familiarity of the I-394 highway before him. Driving back to his downtown hotel with an ache churning around his stomach reminded him he hadn't eaten dinner. He hadn't thought of it until too late, and the run-down neighborhoods he passed didn't offer an open drive-through. Each highway exit lamp created a faster streak past his window, yet none of it mattered to him. The evidence and realization of his lonely state compounded. Over two million people filled the cityscape that drew him, yet, he felt hungry and alone.

He waved his keycard and unlocked the hotel door. The

red blotches around his eyes didn't hold his attention in the entry mirror as much as the blank linen paper across the room did. It almost called to him, resting upon a pristine lacquered desk. Before he tossed his coat and himself on top of the hotel bedspread, the waiting sheet of paper settled his mind for the night.

The sun rays poured their beams over the bedding's fabric, and the shrill morning song of his nightstand alarm lured Gerald out of a soothing sleep. He separated the embossed curtains and revealed a picturesque view. The architecture lifted toward the sky all around him and wedged the room between two high-rises, whose windows reflected the golden sunrise and a sliver of lakeshore. While he felt slightly consoled, he longed for the expanse the glimmering blue waters of Lake Michigan offered. He surrendered a pained sigh, shaved his blonde stubble, and dressed. After patting on his aftershave, Gerald wadded his clothes into his black leather bag and took another hesitant stroll near the desk where the paper and pen laid. The picture window didn't hold his attention this time. Instead, he glided the rolling chair out, lowered himself upon it, and after a pause, began writing like never before.

"Dear Sara,

What do I say to a daughter like you? You have always been a joy to me with your smile and warmth. You have always been there for me with your presence, phone calls, and letters.

Sara, God has truly blessed me with a daughter like you.

Sara, I feel helpless that I cannot take your pain and your illness away from you, that I do not live with you and spend more time with you. You are always in my thoughts and prayers. I want you to know that I love you more than myself and will not give up with my prayers, thoughts, and whatever else I can do…" The letter continued, pen dragging and almost illegible.

"Sara, you have changed my whole idea about what is important. I believe that God has given you a tremendous job to teach me and other people about love and also help save other people. You have been given a big job to help…your family and many others. You cannot give up; you have been given a tremendous opportunity that few people would understand…"

He folded the paper, creased it flat, and sealed it into a monogrammed hotel envelope.

Gerald released his heartfelt words into the lobby's drop-box. Toting his black bag through the revolving glass doors towards the curb, Gerald hesitated to avoid slipping. He finagled his feet over the recent plow of grey snow and disappeared within an airport taxicab for the last time that winter.

***

Arizona's sun-filled days grew sauna-like. After an extended day at the office, Gerald welcomed his jaunt toward the Paradise Valley Country Club. He donned reflective sunglasses, swayed to the smooth notes of the saxophone on his stereo, and allowed every care to fly out his Mustang convertible. Following a workout, he often observed Camelback Mountain on his way to a restaurant for dinner. The music, however, never pumped his spirit up as much as the views of Camelback did. It glowed ruby red, towering before him as the sunset blazed. In those moments, everything felt right in his world. He also loved the feeling of warm wind swirling around his windshield, caressing and cooling his clean damp skin.

Upon arrival in the restaurant's parking lot, Gerald ran a quick shave over his chin and circled up and under his nose.

The white button-down shirt he sported at work earlier in the day waited on the backseat for its retrieval before slipping it on, buttoning it up, and tucking it in. His reflection in the car's finish affirmed what he already knew—he looked great and felt pretty energized for his date.

He strode into the bricked bar area like he owned it and waved to the bartender, recognizing someone he chatted with over the week before.

"Hey, Stan, good to see ya—oh hey…" he said.

He offered a quick nod in return.

Yea, sorry, guy, I don't remember your name.

His steps quickened as he followed the hostess passed high-backed leather benches and the flickering wall lanterns toward his booth. He smiled at the hostess and held her gaze upon receiving his menu. *Oh Yea, I've Still Got It.*

"Thank you, sweetie," he said.

His confidant, tending the bar, continued to swipe and swirl the beer glasses with his white towel. Stan served the patrons kitty-corner to his candlelit table. Gerald enjoyed the location and the ability to connect with his bartender when he didn't feel like pulling up a barstool. He knew Stan remained a shallow substitute for a friend most evenings, but he often needed one. Whenever he arrived, Stan made an effort to listen.

Gerald tipped his wrist and surveyed the time again; this time, he squeezed the back of his neck.

Where is she?

He questioned himself and began to feel his blood pressure rise, peeved by her delay. He scribbled on the napkin before him and tried to distract himself. At that moment, he witnessed his date make a disoriented rush past the hostess while her pink purse dangled from her waving forearm.

"Gerald—," she said.

She slathered him with a breathless description of her travels through traffic and kissed Gerald on the cheek before sliding across the bench opposite him. His eyes questioned the validity of her explanation; it sounded like something he heard a time or two before. Her bright smile consoled him enough to notice the candle's light highlighting her curled brown hair. The jazz playing in the background also soothed any remaining splinter of offense before they ordered their filets. Gerald knew he hadn't known her for more than a few weeks but contemplated over a mixed salad with blue cheese dressing, sharing his whole life with her. As his hand spun a half-empty tumbler, he spoke about Sara, her current treatments, and how much he missed his daughter. Doodling on a napkin once again, he explained in detail the process he considered to bring his daughter to Arizona to see the best specialists. Smiling and nodding often, his date sipped her refilled glass of iced tea. Gerald cleared his throat, observed her attention wandering to those who conversed behind him. The longer the evening drew out, the more she appeared worn and twisted the hair at the base of her neck. She also played with her gold necklace and fussed with her napkin as he spoke. Gerald noticed. He scratched the backside of his head, considering how tired he also felt and thought—— *She's just tolerating me, my regrets, and all this reminiscing.* At the realization of his possible rookie mistake, he remembered things he neglected to tell her about himself and felt like a fraud.

Gerald worked like a madman to pay off compounding debts and medical bills, which made retiring look like a joke. She didn't know he kicked around town, flaunting an appearance he struggled to manage. He hid the truth well. The upscale image that he created breathed down his neck, and he struggled to maintain it every single day. It called and waited to entrap him, as did all the new pressures of Sara's treatment. His uncertain fiscal future loomed over him day and night, compounding his struggle. He often questioned, *How will I balance Illinois visits with Sara, maintain the business to help pay for all the incoming medical bills, and pay the thousands in child support for two teenaged daughters each month?* They pressed like weights upon his already heavy mind, and their shackles prepared to tighten around him at a moment's notice. Gerald began to tremble on the inside. Beads of sweat upon his palms reflected the panic he felt inside. The ice in his tumbler rattled, and he swiped at the sweat near his fingers. Gerald waved toward his attractive waitress for another drink.

After Gerald's refill, he sat up straighter, and his face twisted. Hostile to her indifference and wounded by her lack of engagement, he directed it all in her direction.

"Why are you even here?" He questioned.

She jolted to attention and uncrossed her legs beneath the table.

"Wha—what?" She asked. "I thought we were on a date?

To enjoy each other's company."

Her body squirmed upon the leather surface of her seat.

Gerald's eyes glared at her, suspicious of her intentions.

"Were you even listening to me?" He asked.

"Um, you were talking about your daughter Sara and doctors," She stated.

Ever so slowly, he observed her reach for something next to her. Then, as she placed it upon her lap, he noticed her pull the purse against her stomach. Her cheeked pinked, and her neck became red and blotchy under her collar. Gerald's knee began to bounce. He decided to drive home his offense and resisted the internal reminder to keep his mouth shut.

"You *don't* know what you're talking about...you're so selfish coming here tonight. You didn't even listen to me!" He exclaimed. He realized he repeated himself but didn't care. His face reddened, and his insides seethed. He saw her mouth open, speechless, and watched her slide to the edge of the booth's bench. At that, he sucked down the rest of his refill.

You've had too much to drink, Gerald; say you're wrong, say you're sorry. Get some coffee. He ignored the voice in his head again and waved for his pretty waitress.

"I'll take another."

His date's eyes sparkled by the flicker of candlelight. She sniffed and swallowed hard.

"I think it's time for me to head back and let my dog out. Gerald, thanks for dinner…"

She stood and spun on her high heels before he spoke to her again.

"Yea, run home to your dog," he muttered.

He brushed the encounter off with a sniff, feeling indifferent as he viewed her quick departure. Grabbing for his briefcase, his thumbs clicked the latches open in unison. Gerald didn't fish underneath his file folders for long before he grasped and lifted out a legal pad. Setting it before him upon the table, the bright yellow paper remained blank and silent. Gerald labored to clear his head. His eyes scanned the room, watching couples come and go. He viewed Stan converse with his customers and nodded to him once or twice. He all but emptied his relish tray, crunching carrots, olives, and pepper strips, but left the radishes alone for another day.

Always On My Mind

The woman in the booth in front of him sat tall. Her curls brought Sara's letter to mind again. Twirling the pen, he knew what he had to do. He dropped it and rubbed his face hard between the tips of his fingers. Up until then, he avoided remembering the spiteful words he spoke to his date or the strife. However, once his bill came and he saw the long beverage list before him—he knew. He knew something needed to change. Thoughts prodded him. *Make an effort. Follow through. Take the next right step.*

He placed the pen tip on the paper and began to write, humbled by the loving daughter who hoped to receive his reply to her letter in just a few short days. Sara's memory, her example of strength and grace—warmed him and compelled Gerald to take the deepest of breaths.

"Dear Sara…"

Chapter 5

A Lonely Road

She felt an ache clenching her chest—the days since their father left sunk in. Sara grabbed Putter Paws and squeezed him to her midsection to cough again. At the lengthy string of barks, her mother Susan rounded the corner into the family room and waited until she finished.

"Hey Sara, your dad called earlier; he made it home alright last night," Sara's mother said.

"Oh, good," she stated.

With the assuring news, she pulled the brown afghan up over her shoulders and sank a little deeper into the olive-green recliner.

Sara never envisioned her sophomore year to appear like this. Sitting at length and healing from a tumor surgery ruined her spring break and ruined her sign language church debut. Sara not only felt sorry for herself, she felt sorry for her dad. She knew he hadn't expected any of this to happen either. Disappointments piled up in her thoughts, leading to so many changes for both of them. She tilted her head back on the headrest and shut her eyelids, remembering past disappointments. Sara tried to remember when her parents separated, he left, and they divorced. *He's been gone six years... I'm not the same little girl anymore. He used to protect me, and he doesn't know how anymore. He can't; he can barely take care of himself. Thank you, God. Thank you for keeping him safe going home...* A lone tear slipped down her cheek, and she let it fall.

***

Just two days later, Gerald's note made its way into Sara's mailbox. "Sara, you have a letter from your dad," her mom stated.

Sara hobbled towards the kitchen counter following her bathroom visit. After glancing at his handwriting, she folded and shoved the letter into her back pocket for a later read.

Not long after, while her mom made Swedish Pancakes for dinner, Sara consumed her father's written words. Her heart drummed with hope. This new connection through the mail thrilled her. With a gentle grasp of the letter, Sara stroked the page, reading and rereading it before she responded with another letter of her own.

A Lonely Road

"Dear Dad,

Hello, how are you? I'm still pretty sore. My back is really sore; because when I walk, I kind of have to walk hunched over. I'm really trying hard to stand up straight. I've been trying to walk a little more each day to stretch out the incision.

Ever since this has happened, everything seems so unreal, like I'm in a dream—some things good, some things bad. It's so weird because ever since this has happened, TONS of people from our past have suddenly popped up and have come in contact with us. It's really great to hear from everybody. It's kind of sad, though, that something so drastic has to happen to bring everybody together. A lot of my old grade school friends want to come visit me, and the neighbors on the corner sent me flowers today. It made me feel happy. I got a lot of cards today, like from your brother and Aunt Barbara and Uncle Harold. I don't know what to do about trying to figure out arrangements for visiting and stuff. I've been thinking about it. We'll talk more next week. I love you and miss you bunches. Talk to you later——

Love in Christ,

Sara

P.S. Remember to stay strong, and so will I."

Sara sank the folded paper into the new envelope and fanned herself with it. She grinned, thankful, feeling as if she wanted to fly. She liked knowing how her dad felt and being there for him, even though many states separated them. The joy, however, didn't alleviate the salivation under her tongue. She felt a slight wave of nausea. Breathing through it, she acknowledged the responsibility. She felt it, and its pressure weighed heavy, maybe even heavier than healing from the tumor surgery. *He needs help. He needs encouragement. God, how can I focus on both my healing and his need too?* She crossed her arms and warmed herself. At one time, many lighthearted fifteen-year-old thoughts circled her mind. Now, she wondered about things she'd never put to paper like——*Who's there for you in Arizona, Dad? Who's comforting you when you go home after a long day? Or when you sit alone in your office, who do you talk to? It's okay, Dad; it's okay—keep writing to me, and it'll give me the focus, hope, and the determination I need to write you back, get better, and travel to Arizona to visit you. I won't be able to take horseback riding lessons again—but we could enjoy our long talks face to face… and maybe a short walk at the foot of your mountain if you hold my arm and keep me steady...*

***

Sara sat on her bedside and bounced just enough to express her excitement to Dyane, who sat across from her laughing. Feeling a bit weak, she enjoyed their latest window of opportunity to re-connect alone before Dyane and Joseph's return to Michigan. Both of them nestled themselves within a nest of Sara's get-well gifts and cards. Sara pleaded Dyane for her help reorganizing everything in her hope chest. While they began sorting and organizing—Sara felt a few thoughts gnawing at her.

"So, I need to tell you something. Maybe you can help me know what to do? So, earlier this year, when all the doctor stuff and surgery was going on, and then I recovered, one of my better friends, Lissa, agreed to hang out. But, here's the problem, I don't want to talk about guys much anymore with her. And, I get way more tired than I used to, so we're shopping together at the mall less. I honestly don't want to shop anymore, really. Oh, and I'm really starting to feel irritated with her ungrateful attitude, ya know? Like, she's got an awesome life and family, but she thinks everything's a crisis. I'm losing my patience. Maybe it's because she's talking about our friend's situations, and either I don't want to hear about it from her, or maybe I'm feeling jealous—I don't know. My nerves can't take it anymore, I guess..."

Dyane stared at her and nodded.

"I know, it all sounds weird," Sara stated with a nervous laugh. "Shopping at the mall used to be great, talking about boys and my friends too. I guess I'm just not feeling like the old me anymore."

Dyane cleared her throat and smiled this time. She set the stack of cards she held back onto the carpet. Then, scooted a little closer to Sara.

"Hey, you mean to tell me you feel like you're changing? Yes, I see it too. You are *growing,* Sara. Letting go of what was, to focus on the things ahead of you. The things that truly last. But, having less in common with one of your best friends breaks my heart."

Sara's shoulders rounded forward.

"Yea, mine too," she stated.

"Sara, I see that. I saw the tears in your eyes as you spoke about her. I'm so sorry. I'm sorry you may need to sacrifice more than you already have. Man, you're growing up into a woman before my eyes!" Dyane said.

Her playful tap on Sara's leg made them both smile.

"May I pray for you both?" Dyane asked.

Sara nodded. She dropped her head and exhaled, thankful her big sister understood because to her, it didn't come out sounding right.

"Oh Father, thank you for my baby sister, who's growing up so, so, fast. She isn't the same sister who tortured me over the TV remote or my boyfriends in high school or the same one who obsessed over high school dances and longed to turn sixteen just to date. God, please give Sara more grace for her fifteen-year-old friend. I pray they won't give up on each other and allow cancer or anything else to rob them of friendship. Please help them work it out, and both grow in you. May these sisters in Christ soon share things in common once again. In Jesus' name, Amen."

Sara's prior disappointment gave way into a softened expression and a grateful smile as she felt Dyane's hand lift off of her shoulder. Sara looked into Dyane's eyes; then, at an ocean of cards and piles of gifts, she remembered her family's support, her churches, her schools, the circle of friends that loved her, and God's presence; Sara felt more loved than she ever had before. Once Sara told Dyane how many pieced of mail she received in a day, her sister sat speechless. She loved watching Dyane become the student, gaining a first-hand education on how much a card or letter meant to someone like her.

Each afternoon things continued to arrive by mail, assuring her soul, she still mattered. After lunch, she tugged at glued flaps with eagerness and sipped in every written word while balancing upon a barstool at the kitchen counter. With a few unopened in her hand, she carried them up to her room and stretched her legs under her bedcovers to read more. Afterward, she tucked them into her hope chest among the others. Sara treasured their uplifting words, the outpours of love, and every morsel of lasting encouragement. Sara's relief often told the whole story. The doubt, worry, and fear fled in the presence of such encouragement. Sara now understood a very precious thing; true gifts of God's grace, undeserved and unsolicited. God used them every day to strengthen Sara to press on, keep going, and continue the fight of her life.

***

A Lonely Road

The doorbell chimed. As soon as Susan opened the door, an unexpected visitor caught Sara off guard. She tried to calm her barking cocker spaniel and locked the swinging gate behind her as she came up behind her mom. Sara glanced toward the door after overhearing the brief exchange. She noticed the woman nodded at Susan and shifted from one foot to another.

"I need to speak with Sara Schreck, please," the dark-haired woman at the door stated.

The woman's boldness appeared to take Susan off guard. She nodded, clearing her throat with apprehension before allowing Sara to replace her at the door. Sara took hold of the storm door's handle as her mother receded back down the hallway towards the kitchen.

"Sara, I recently heard that you have cancer. I felt I must come and must tell you—I believe if you have more faith, you will get well," the woman stated.

Sara paused, waiting for more words from the woman who didn't smile at her. Sara didn't know what to say in return for her statement or her silence. She felt the heat climb up the front of her neck, and she did not know why. The woman's eyes searched Sara's. Maybe the woman misunderstood her pause, or maybe she felt a twinge of regret, but all Sara mustered to say in return after a few long seconds tumbled out.

"Okay, thanks. Um, thanks for coming by."

Sara swung the red door shut, allowing it to slam without realizing it. She shuffled into the kitchen, feeling puzzled and hurt. Dyane held a palm upon her stomach at hearing what the woman spoke over her, and everyone in the room appeared disturbed. They listened but said little after their initial questions. Sara plopped onto a stool and hung her head. Her mom began to rub her back, and her thumbs untangled the tension that squeezed the base of her neck. The woman's words stung under the assumption she lacked any faith to get well. Sara wondered how she learned about her cancer. Then she wondered—*Did Catherine tell her? Or she read about it in that thirty-two-church newsletter update?* Thinking about it made her face hot with embarrassment. She raised the back of her hand and felt her face, wondering if anyone else noticed. Even though church families wanted these updates, it still stunned her. Grateful—barely described how Sara, not to mention her family, felt about the support. Yet, internal questions remained. *Did this random stranger take it upon herself to speak these words on her own?* The whole experience remained a mystery—*a frustrating mystery.* Maybe she meant well, but Sara felt disheartened by the whole exchange on her front porch that day.

The woman's words cut into her psyche, and Sara's mind continued to shout and question—*She isn't God, and she doesn't know me! Doesn't man look at the outward appearance, and only God see the heart?* Nevertheless, deep inside her core, Sara wondered if the woman's words rang true and how the Bible might speak to this situation?

For days, weeks, and months in the days to follow, she wrestled with her personal faith in God's healing. "If you don't have enough faith," Sara heard the woman say, "you won't get well." The words twisted in her head. The sentence she remembered replayed over and over again in Sara's mind, and its ever-expanding accusation spat in her face. Months before, Sara knew what Dyane's full-blown reaction to the implying words might've held. However, her big sister's feelings remained steady, and it confused her. Had she misunderstood something about the woman's words? Sara pondered the changes she saw in Dyane and struggled to follow her sister's new example. She stared at Dyane over a magazine, gladdened to see the difference in her sister's calmer reaction.

The lesson helped her realize something. People, even sincere church-going people, miscommunicate or misunderstand. Sometimes, they not only hold the capability of disheartening the weak but also may plant seeds of doubt by accident. Either way, like her sister, she also desired to grow in better communication and in her grace for others. She felt drawn to make better choices. It also became clear; she needed to forgive this woman rather than hold a grudge. Sara knew deep down Dyane wanted to fix it, but instead, she allowed her big sister to console her. Dyane's warm arms tightened around Sara's shrinking shoulders, and she felt accepted again. Sara also felt encouraged by her truthful counsel and knew a sister hug waited for her as often as she needed one. This encouragement painted a smile upon Sara's face. It also made it easier to place her internal conflict all in God's hands and let it go.

Chapter 6

Embracing The Unknown

In moments alone, Dyane sipped steaming peach tea. Her dachshund Kirby circled the seat of the floral chair before curling into a ball. Dyane sighed. Streams of sunlight backlit the green Michigan pines outside her window. Friday mornings always offered a bittersweet respite from her work at the oak furniture store below their apartment. The spicy candle at the center of her farm table flickered near her peanut butter-slathered bagel. She fanned the pages of her Bible to 2 Corinthians 1:5 and read it out loud as if to proclaim what she believed against the invisible robber of their peace. *"For just as the sufferings of Christ flow over into our lives, so also through Christ our comfort overflows."* She clung to the words. This truth still offered comfort and a shield to her mind. Dyane picked up her tea and blew the steam away before sipping. Her ongoing forgiveness of Sara's well-meaning stranger required a daily decision for Dyane. She reached for her bagel and sunk her teeth into the soft, buttery crust. However, the more she chewed, the more she began to feel queasy. Whether the bagel or the thoughts firing in her head, she knew she needed to breathe deep until her wave of perspiration evaporated. The stranger's well-meaning intentions still gnawed at her. Yet, she purposed to believe God for His ongoing comfort. His keen awareness of Sara's need remained. Dyane trusted Him, and she still felt grateful for the assurance of His promises, believing He'd help her forgive this woman fully. Dyane didn't claim perfection but remembered His mercy and how often God's grace showed up to help her. Dyane also misspoke at times, so full forgiveness of another doing the same required her extension of grace also. At that moment, above a little oak furniture store within Bailey, Michigan, Dyane chose to surrender the words the woman spoke to her little sister Sara once and for all. She bent her head, placed it into God's hands, and forgave Sara's stranger that very day.

***

"You are going to become *Auntie Sara* in January…" Dyane and her husband Joseph sung in unison.

Dyane drew the phone's receiver away from their ears.

Embracing the Unknown

They giggled at the high-pitched squeals from the other end of the phone line. *Thank you, God, thank you, thank you.* Dyane's knee swung, and her heart fluttered with joy. Dyane and Joseph's dancing eyes met; then, Dyane shivered with delight while sharing such good news with Sara and returned the phone to her ear. After a few months of IVs, chemo treatments, draining hospital stays, and lonely afternoons at home, Sara now grasped something spectacular to look forward to.

The preparation underway for their first child's birth, as well as their family's first grandchild on both sides, triggered a long-distance planning frenzy. In the meantime, Joseph and Dyane made multiple trips back and forth from Michigan to Illinois that summer to participate in Sara's life. On the drawn-out weeks they failed to visit, her cancer treatment progress came by phone. While Dyane reveled the comfort each update brought from her mom, her heart more than ached to remain a significant part of Sara's new routine and her treatments.

One afternoon, while Dyane prepared pasta and turkey meatballs for dinner, Joseph's early appearance took her by surprise.

"Hey, hun," he greeted.

Weariness slanted his ocean-blue eyes, clothed his words while he kissed her cheek, and her heart fluttered as she hugged him in return. He allowed his arms to fall sooner than she expected and turned his face away from her gaze. Dyane fixed her eyes on the back of his head and reached to grab the two placemats out of the drawer near them. He leaned into the countertop, and their eyes met.

"It's over," Joseph stated.

Her eyes searched his expression and widened—"What's over?"

Just as she began to ask, his eyes watered and broke their connection by diverting his attention out the window. Redness crept up his neck and flooded his cheeks. Joseph held his breaths for moments longer than the one before it and exhaled a fragmented answer to Dyane's question. The rubbing of his forehead prohibited her from hearing him fully.

"Joseph, what?" She pleaded, seeking to understand.

"Well, I'm not sure, Chuck called me into his office, and he said a student's parent didn't like how I coordinated the last church youth event. She spoke with Chuck on the side, and Chuck spoke to the elders without my knowing. They invited me into a meeting tonight after work, and I sat there so confused. I pressed Chuck for an answer as to why this parent hadn't come to me directly. If my reason for attending the elder's meeting regarded the budget, then it made sense or even the growth of our youth group or children's ministry. They are both growing—."

At that, his eyes filled, and he swiped both eyes with the back of his forearm. The confusing but definite explanation sent Dyane into a panic.

"No, *no!*"

She reached for him as she surrounded the counter. Her throat began to reduce to a pinhole—too tight to speak anymore, much less breathe. They wrapped their arms around each other as their tears fell. The scenario felt all too familiar. Joseph buried his face into Dyane's short hair, and she allowed a storeroom of tears to sink into his cotton button-up shirt. Their second ministry—over. Just like that. Dyane didn't speak, but plenty of words raced through her mind—*Over. Done. Finished. We got rid of our boxes... Why, why, did we get rid of our boxes? What are we going to do? What are we going to do? We can't move farther away from home—Sara needs us; we need her! Lord Jesus, have mercy—what are we going to do?* The alarm and anger she once let go of as they departed their Florida ministry—began to resurface. Then, it turned into frustration, shock and began to overwhelm her mind. Joseph's body deflated as he lowered his body onto the closest dining chair to where he stood while holding Dyane as she sobbed.

"Shh Dy, we will make it, we will somehow," He said.

While Joseph caressed her hair, she envisioned those they loved in their church family—every student, every parent, every dear friend. *How do we explain something we don't even understand ourselves?* It felt like the worst possible time to lose a job with Sara so sick and their first baby on the way. *Oh no—our baby arrives eight months from now! God, is this a joke?* Dyane almost shot up off of Joseph's lap and stomped her foot in defiance—she didn't want to move any farther away than she already felt from her family. Almost too much for her to accept, she wondered if people viewed youth minister's jobs as disposable and wondered why no one warned them before moving all over the United States. Fear and faith both battled for her mind. Her heart pounded like the waves of thoughts she fought off. Dyane struggled to respond. She also struggled to protect her husband from feeling this loss, this injustice, this blow to his identity. She squeezed him tighter. Dyane cried, enveloped in her own weakness, and felt her body's deflation. Her inner fight began to dissipate only as she remembered who their battle belonged to. Wads of tissues still collected on the table, however, before she realized she needed to lay down.

***

Days later, their local job search ensued. Multiple fears repeated and raced through her head and closed in fast as they discussed their options. They agreed full-time ministry hindered any luxury of flying back to Illinois for every chemo treatment or surgery. Soon after, Joseph crossed off many newspaper leads in Michigan—and after the last door shut, they both surrendered to reality.

Joseph and Dyane struggled with the next firm step before them, admitting their need to Dyane's parents with hopes of returning to their home. Dyane's parents never hesitated. So, they packed up the moving truck again—but alone this time. None of those eager to move them in came back to help pack or load their truck. No one checked in, gave them hugs, or wished them well. It broke Dyane's heart into a thousand pieces to step off of their apartment steps for the last time. Joseph helped hoist Dyane up onto a slippery seat and then placed their sedated pooch upon her shrinking lap. Dyane lifted her head up towards their closed front door, sipping in one final glance. She didn't know how to feel about it all. Dyane feared the church's thoughts over their abandonment as Joseph resigned himself to the will of the elders, regardless of the clarity. It grieved them both to no end.

Goodbye donut shop, train depot, Sherry's diner, beautiful Victorian with your white porch, church, evergreen, the lake where we enjoyed many church picnics... Dyane didn't hold enough tissues to collect the tears from her lips and chin fast enough. She scanned the rearview mirror without her glasses one last time. Nothing but the growling sound of the diesel engine proclaimed their departure from the town of two hundred that morning. No waves goodbye sent them on their way. The truck's fumes made Dyane feel queasy. She watched the familiar signs pass them by on the highway in a smear of trees, buildings, and increasing traffic. Among the bumps in the road, Dyane felt weary but grateful for her mom and Jim's grace once again. She knew any parent willing to open their two-car garage for a second time for their moving storage deserved quite an award.

Dyane's grandmother prepared for their arrival with enthusiasm, and Sara assured her she'd wait at the window. Almost four hours after their departure, Joseph dragged the truck trailer up into their driveway and slid out of the cab. He appeared sheepish and embarrassed as he hugged those waiting for them. The second time they moved back to Dyane's parent's home weighed heavier on her. Dyane's shame melted, though, with every hug, kiss, and smile that welcomed them home to Illinois that day. All this answer to prayer didn't look like the hopeful vision she carried in her head. However, this moment encapsulated some things far better. God provided. God made a way. God ministered to her loss. And God brought them home where they belonged.

Dyane lay upon a new bed and watched her beautiful belly lift and collapse. In those moments, she also took comfort in the familiar gong of her grandmother's grandfather clock and the creaks from the ceiling above where her fifteen-year-old sister, Sara, climbed into her bed for the night. As Dyane drifted off to sleep with Joseph nestled into her side, she prayed in the silence—*Thank you, Father, that every good and perfect gift does come from you. It truly does. You did work all this out, and now we may look forward to playing a part in Sara's life every day. I made wrong choices. I'm sorry I panicked and complained. I'm sorry I didn't trust you early on to take care of us like you did before—it's a gift to be home…*

***

Each day, opportunities arose for Dyane to encourage and mentor Sara in her faith. Dyane loved their long talks together about what God communicated with her and the opportunities to even guide Sara to Bible passages that helped with what she went through. Because of the storms Sara endured over a few years before, it felt like Dyane's daily presence mattered more than it ever did in the past to both of them. Dyane also discovered that while she lived out her new purpose with her sister, Sara grew in maturity and began to live out her own purpose—in spite of cancer.

It became clear that all of the losses soon gave way to new opportunities. In God's perfect timing and plan, Dyane became free to attend almost all of Sara's hospital appointments and chemo treatments. She also took some overnight shifts during Sara's weeklong stays in the pediatric ward. The regular bonding moments between Sara, Elizabeth, Dyane, their mom Susan, and grandma Irene grew more priceless over those months. Rebuilt trust and joy clothed them.

A few nurses, especially a spunky one named Maribeth, began to take notice. They began to draw some attention at the hospital once again. After they entered the hospital building, people watched their three-generational cluster with interest—especially as they stepped onto the pediatric floor. Dyane also began to observe a behavioral shift with Sara's nurses. They began to hang out in Sara's room, laughing, teasing and tending her needs a little longer whenever Sara's female entourage spent time at the hospital. The sterile silence soon became a rarity because, over a short period of time, Sara Schreck developed into quite a popular patient.

Daylight, conversation, and the sun's reflection off the taller windows from nearby buildings, often filled Sara's room until Dr. White rounded the doorway. On one particular day, he glided in with a clipboard in hand and wore a stony expression. Jim, Sara's stepfather, gave a respectful welcome, met his gaze with his own, and stretched out his hand for a firm shaking. After leaning over to take a closer look at Sara, Dr. White sat rigid and stiffened at the end of Sara's bed. Their family, however, rested on the cold vinyl chairs they stole from nearby rooms. Sara's glanced over at her forty-three-year-old mom as she reached up toward her ears and spun a miniature dial upon her hearing aids. A smile their grandma wore just moments before disappeared. Her wrinkled eyes smoothed out and grew larger, her eyebrows slanted with worry, and her lips thinned into a line. It felt as if a butterfly had entered Dyane's stomach, and she shivered with a chill. Her stepfather stepped back and stood against a wall, his elbows locked straight and his fists stuffed deep inside his pockets. In the doctor's dry manner, he glanced at Sara, her mom, and Jim over his wire-rimmed glasses and spoke of Sara's upcoming chemo regiment.

"Do you have any questions for me?" he asked. Sara tipped her head in suspicion and glared at her doctor with intensity.

"Am I going to lose my hair with that chemo?" she asked.

Dr. White clicked his pen twice, tapped it on his clipboard, and appeared to weigh the words inside his head. Then, he gave Sara a blunt but honest answer.

"Yes," he said.

After a long pause, she peered at him and suggested a different plan to the head of the Rush Oncology Department.

"Can we try a different chemo?" she asked.

Embracing the Unknown

To Dyane, Sara's question sounded less like a question and more like a suggestive statement. However, the doctor's measured response gave Sara no comfort or ease. She sank backward against the stack of pillows with a deep but quiet sigh. Dyane watched Sara as she stared at the stiff white blanket she twisted between her fingers. The answer dropped like a rock into Dyane's stomach. Her mind also reeled from the idea of Sara bald as the doctor spoke about the new portacath implant they prepared for. It meant another surgery and a valve insertion below the skin's surface, just underneath Sara's collarbone. Dr. White answered questions from both Sara's mom and stepfather, but while Sara listened to their voices, her face paled to a pasty white. As their conversation continued, Dyane's thoughts created a strange blend of muffled voices.

***

In March, Sara began taking oral chemotherapy, but before her monthly cycle returned in April, Sara often dropped into bed fatigued and suffering from excruciating headaches. The portacath surgery remained nerve-racking for everyone and left a bulge under a thin layer of her flesh. Dyane overheard her mom assure and remind Sara that in the long run, it diminished excessive needle poking into her veins. Sara didn't see it as a gift as her mom did. Not one of them wanted her to become a human pincushion.

After her first inpatient chemotherapy lasted for five to six days, and she returned home, Dyane overheard her mom laughing in the kitchen after she hung up her coat. While Susan spoke with Grandma Irene in the kitchen, she described Sara's abnormal reaction to chemo—

"Nothing keeps her down," she stated.

She described the scene she came upon in the bathroom a few days after Sara arrived home from her first chemo treatment.

"So, while I got ready for Jim to come home from work, Sara meandered in, pulled her makeup bag out of the cabinet, and began to primp and prepare to attend that concert with the youth group. I hadn't seen her in make-up for so long that I stood there mesmerized. Each application of blush and shadow just magnified her beautiful features."

Dyane pictured her innocent blue eyes brightening, her petite powdered nose, and dabs of shimmering pink lipstick—it all drew attention to her thinned face. The joy she wore that night, her mom said, beautified her most of all.

Embracing the Unknown

Dyane imagined her, immersed in the evening as just one girl out of many in the arena blending into the crowd. A river of darkness, the streaming spotlights, the familiar melodies pounding within her chest—all reminding her sister of truths she struggled to remember on her own. On this evening, however, accompanied by friends from church, Dyane prayed every single song and moment mattered to Sara. She hoped, within a bursting arena, every distraction of cancer fell away. Whether her bald head, the chemicals pumping at will throughout her veins, their effects, or a weakened body, she prayed nothing hindered her. Among an ocean of souls, Dyane desired for her sister to render her heart to Jesus once again. To choose to truly live every day for the lover of her soul, as her last. Dyane knew Sara's personal revival didn't depend upon her giving the best advice to her sister, praying the perfect prayer, or even a musician's fanfare. The next steps in her sister's faithfulness belonged to Sara alone.

Dyane hungered to respond with her own arms raised and sing at the top of her lungs also, uncaring what her voice sounded like in a crowd. She knew life's darkness enveloped her sister daily, but the boldness of Dyane's prayer that night ignited a personal desire for Sara's transformation. *Father, please, combat any discouragement within my sister with truth, worship, faith, and the joy of your Holy Spirit. Amen!*

***

The long autumn gave way to treatments through Thanksgiving, a Christmas break, and then the New Year. The bitter wintery months that followed the concert pressed in, and as expected, the thief of their joy didn't waste a minute to make an entrance. Praising, lifting her arms, and smiling, became a struggle for Sara over those long grey months and every worship song faded to faint, prayerful whispers. Sara's reaction to the intravenous poison overwhelmed her body without escape, and one thing became clear—Sara's family felt tempted to fear the worst. A fever swooped in, burned like an internal fire, knocking her down without any warning. Dyane's family began to clear their spring calendars again, and one thing remained clear, controlling the May calendar proved impossible as well. It rushed in, and Sara ended her junior year of high school by moving her belongings into the hospital and surrendering to her newest reality—living at the hospital for longer lengths of time. Weeks of chemotherapy rounds began to take their heaviest toll on everyone. With a hospital discharge date unknown and poor white blood and kidney count, Sara remained there indefinitely.

Embracing the Unknown

As each day passed, Sara's weariness multiplied, and she appeared to allow herself to succumb to it a little more. She became quieter for longer periods of time. Fluids pulsed through the IV tubes while she lay on a rock-hard hospital bed, the medications flushed through her body, and she underwent many twenty-four-hour urine tests. Day after day, every intravenous antibiotic, blood draw, physical exam— stripped Sara of her modesty, her youth, her normal teenaged routine, and aged her beyond her peers. This weighty reality became her newest normal—taking one step forward and a few backward. This upward hike around daily obstacles proved exhausting, spiritually challenging, and often painful beyond Sara's ability to express.

Chapter 7

Hiding and Seeking

Susan braced herself as Monday arrived. She spun the vertical blinds open, and they clattered together, announcing the new week. Daylight poured in, illuminating her way toward the kitchen counter where Susan's day always began. Hand stenciled grapevines, painted by her sister Judy, gracefully strung themselves across the soffit above her head. The dishes done the night before pleased her, as well as the clutter Jim had cleared from the tile countertops just before she rose for the day. The organized beginning of her morning routine brought greater peace to the thoughts bombarding her mind.

As Susan hung up the phone, an outburst of elation caused her cocker spaniel to jump up upon her leg. Her pen then scratched a memo upon her already cluttered calendar— *CT Scan—chemo working! Yay!* Welling tears distorted the numbers as she pressed them into the phone. It felt good for

Susan to proclaim the good news, and one by one, drips of happiness splashed down upon her notes. While she made her way down the call list, she hoped for many hearts to burst as her own did over the answers to prayer. She refused to ignore the brilliant gleam within their growing nightmare.

However, on May 26th, Sara's sixteenth birthday, the short-lived celebration ended when Sara entered the hospital with another fever. Weak and in a wheelchair, she rolled into the familiar carpet-stained corridor. At the elevator, Susan readjusted a blanket around Sara's sweatered shoulders and placed a cool hand upon her forehead. Sara shivered underneath it, and goosebumps proceeded to cover her arms. Her daughter's head drooped, Susan knew this failed to hit the mark of what they envisioned for celebrating Sara's birthday. The lit numbers above the elevators dimmed in a mute countdown. Before its chime, Jim released the wheelchair's handles and guided Susan's weary body closer to his side.

An inner battle began to stir up again. Susan tried to take each thought captive, but the effort grew all too real and exhausting. She glided alongside Sara near a stretch of windows that overlooked the United Center, and instead of admiring the skyline for the thousandth time, she observed her daughter's sight fixed straight ahead. Jim twisted the squeaking wheels down a long echoing tunnel before they arrived at the pediatric wing. Susan rushed a little before them and tapped the silver wheelchair button on the light geometric patterned wall. The double doors swung open and swallowed them. They progressed alone until the doors closed behind them. A hoopla of singing, shouts from the nurse's station seized their gaze and jolted Sara upon her seat. Susan smiled and set her warm hand on her daughter's shoulder.

"Happy birthday, Sara!" they exclaimed.

Familiar nurses greeted her as the chair paraded down the festive and colorful hallway.

"Oh, my word, thank you guys—thank you…you didn't have to…" Balloons of hot pink, yellow, and purple enveloped her rolling chair. Sara laughed and grazed her hand along the streaming cords Susan held near her armrest, separating the strands without realizing it.

"Thank you, oh thank you…" Sara said in a small voice.

As her stepdad Jim continued rolling the wheelchair down towards her room, Sara's face began to flush. Multitasking, Susan strolled with nurses Laura and Beth while keeping a close eye on her daughter.

"What a beautiful cake!" She exclaimed.

Susan picked up her pace once she realized Sara didn't drool over it at all. Her daughter needed a bathroom far more and to climb into bed. Hurrying, Susan reached up to touch Sara's warm forehead again, then viewed a collection of goosebumps appear upon Sara's pale arms. She shivered before Susan yanked up her falling blanket.

Susan's eyes slanted, and she scratched her head with a long unpainted fingernail. Sara's coverlet of half-enthusiastic smiles and waves during the festivities confused her. To her mother, she appeared to put off the nausea and fever well. Susan, however, failed to veil her own anxiety. She blew air through her lips and felt tempted to rip the slow-rolling wheelchair handles from her husband. Almost to room 212, she resisted releasing her mama bear. Susan, instead, directed a quiet impatient growl toward Jim under her breath.

"Move faster," she stated.

His hands began to tremble, and he squeezed the grips tighter.

The rubbing swoosh of the rubber tires came to a halt as they entered her new room. His foot locked the wheels in place before his shaky adjustment of the wheelchair. Jim then stepped into the hallway and disappeared. Susan honed in on her daughter's countenance. Sara bounced her eyes from the sidewall to the north wall above her bed. Posters hung by strips of tape clung to the concrete walls, streamers dangled in various twists of primary colors, and her nurse already folded the bed blankets back to snuggle down into. Sara's mom slid her winter coat down her arms and deposited it upon the bedrail. Susan hurried herself and held her breath while Sara's teeth chattered. Supported from the side while Susan folded up Sara's stripped bulky clothes layers, Sara began to shake. Faded and pilled, the light hospital gown slipped up over Sara's arms, and Susan finished dressing her by tying the gown's flapping backside. Her gentle hand slipped up and underneath Sara's armpit, then lowered and guided Sara's hunched body into a sitting position upon the mattress. Due to its thickness, it remained quite still while Sara lifted her chilled and pale legs onto the bed. Sara's teeth chattered. Susan strove to nestle her daughter's body down between the scratchy white sheets and drape the few thin blankets over her. She watched her daughter's response. With a swift turn, Susan untangled the cord from the plastic arm rail and pressed the nurse red call button hard.

"May I help you?" a woman questioned.

"Yes, we need more blankets in here quickly, please," Susan stated.

Susan found it difficult to forget the purple patterned lines indented into her daughter's skin. They appeared even darker in the fluorescent lighting that evening. Susan pulled at the pillows which sat against the faux wood headboard and tucked the covers underneath Sara's legs.

At that moment, the nighttime nurse shuffled into the room with the folded warm blankets. Susan received them with a sigh of relief.

"Thank you so much," she said.

Jim returned to the room while she layered them on the surface of Sara's body, which then nuzzled in underneath a blaring light. Susan reached for the light string and yanked it. With Sara's blue eyes still shut tight, Susan didn't expect to see them for the rest of the night.

Jim approached his wife's side and handed her a large cup of ice.

"I'm sorry for my impatience," she stated.

He reached for her, and they held each other longer and tighter than they had all week.

"I forgive you," Jim replied.

Their rushing ceased, the crowd dissipated, and nothing else mattered in those moments. Warm tingles traveled up Susan's spine.

"I love you," Susan said.

"I love you," replied him.

They kissed twice and exchanged a grin.

"I'll come back in the morning. You good?" he questioned.

"Yes, I am. Would you help me move out the recliner so I may make it up, though?" she asked.

Without hesitation, Jim finagled the heavy recliner forward.

"Thanks, honey," Susan said.

"You're welcome; I'm going to head out now," he stated.

Till That Day Comes

Smiling, he kissed her again, squeezed her hand, and Susan welcomed the lightness of her own heart. At the door, they exchanged waves and blew a few extra kisses into the air.

Susan gathered her toiletry bag and prepped herself for the night. She brushed her teeth, put on her pajamas, made up her own bed on the recliner, shut the curtains to block the highway's headlights, and flipped the light switch. Minus the brightness bursting underneath the door, room 212 dimmed to black.

In the wee hours, Susan awoke to nurses changing out Sara's fluid bags and administering medication. Sara groaned, and Susan's eyes strained to focus upon the nurse's shadow standing next to the bedside. Susan's eyeglasses rested upon the rolling nightstand, and her blurred grogginess proved difficult to shake. Once coherent, she saw Sara hold out her hand and swallow her pills before her daughter laid down to sleep again. Susan peered past Sara's IV pole to check her blankets and yawned. Then, she sat forward and stretched her back from right to left before her spine sank against the back of the recliner again. Comforting and peaceful thoughts swaddled Susan's soul in the darkness. No stranger to sacrifice, Susan endured the discomfort of the recliner to bring her baby girl the peace she needed.

Hiding and Seeking

In the twilight, strange hospital noises penetrated the denseness of the door, but with Susan's hearing aids in their case, she didn't stir. Carts squeaked down the hallway. Shrilling alarms triggered without warning. Conversations in daytime pitches proceeded past their room, faded, and Susan's slight snore muffled any other remaining sound.

Sometimes, Sara startled awake and called her mom in the hospital room because she forgot where she slept. Because of this, Susan often stood at her kitchen counter during the week with a phone attached to her ear. She made phone calls, arranged, and rearranged her schedule to coordinate an overnight hospital sleeping routine. It seemed to Susan, whenever Sara spent a night at the hospital with family or friends, it felt like a slumber party to her. With every overnight, regardless of the physical challenges, Sara's countenance always appeared brighter to Susan upon her return to the hospital in the morning. Whether in the hospital for chemo, a fever, or an infection, Sara's spirit rejoiced, and Susan witnessed her strength renewed because of the company.

The written overnight sleeping schedule Susan laid out in her planner appeared as; *Dyane or Mom—Monday, Tuesday—?, Wednesday—Elizabeth, Thursday—Grandma, Friday—Elizabeth, Saturday—Dyane, and Sunday—Friend.*

123

Till That Day Comes

After Sara returned home from the threat of another infection, her doctor sent back strict instructions with Susan—to take it easy and lay low. Sara obeyed both mother and doctor by welcoming the rest in her own bed on the first day. As if vacationing on a remote island, she settled into a simpler routine far from poking needles, curious interns, and the sterile environment she frequented.

Pausing, Susan observed Sara tucked into the soft green family room chair, covered with a heavy afghan her Grandma Irene crocheted. She also noticed Sara embraced a new hobby—people watching from that seat. Susan enjoyed her daughter's growth, her attentiveness, as well as her newfound contentment at home to heal. Sara often glanced from her nest-like perch, entertained by the simplest of moments. Exchanged gazes with others from across the room readily met Sara's return smile.

It didn't matter if the phone rang, if the TV played, or if their dog Molly barked at a backyard squirrel—Susan witnessed Sara enjoy her simplified daytime routine of being still. Obvious to most, she didn't want to miss any of the hustle or bustle. Compared to the confining hospital room, the noisy family life excited her. For the first time, Susan acknowledged Sara's contentment. Family and friends often popped in to say hello. Greeting cards also arrived in their mailbox daily, and Susan's routine meals satisfied Sara's pallet enough to receive a thank you before she left the table.

Rest provided the time for the healing of Sara's body, emotional outlook, family relationships, as well as an increased attachment to God. Days later, alone in Sara's quiet bedroom while putting away her laundry, Susan took notice of a cracked open hefty black book upon her nightstand. Gliding her fingertips over the words with care, she understood. The changes in her daughter reflected what she read. Sara believed and applied the words to her life. The words also spoke directly to her and answered the questions that pressed upon her own mind in recent days. She needed guidance, and there it jumped off of the page. Ink marked Matthew 5:13-16 in the margin of Sara's Bible.

You are the salt of the earth. But if the salt loses its saltiness, how can it be made salty again? It is no longer good for anything, except to be thrown out and trampled by men. You are the light of the world. A city on a hill cannot be hidden. Neither do people light a lamp and put it under a bowl. Instead they put it on its stand, and it gives light to everyone in the house. In the same way, let your light shine before men, that they may see your good deeds and praise your Father in heaven.

Susan caught herself observing Sara's illumination more in the days following. It seemed to her, Sara's probing the Bible for answers—enlivened sown seeds which soon sprung up and revealed themselves. Over the years, Susan knew God worked the soil of her little family's hearts. He sent those who planted truths—family members, church family, pastors, and her Christian high school teachers. To her mom, the sparkle inside Sara reflected something ignited. Mindful, Susan carried those captivated thoughts into Sara's next hospital stay.

Susan welcomed the time together, after her coordinated scheduling efforts, the simplest things in their life quickly elevated into the best things of all. She asked her mom Irene for less hospital assistance during the day and now felt freed to invest her time elsewhere. Jim gained an extra midday phone call. Lessening time with Sara allowed for more engagement with Dyane and Elizabeth, as well as unrushed lunches with her mom and a movie or shopping day trip with her best friend Joy. However, Susan felt both pleased by the changes and a little mom guilt just the same. She didn't want to miss any transformation in her youngest daughter. So, she embraced her wild little sanguine often and enjoyed Sara's expanded wisdom and input as well. These treasures bred more gratefulness between them.

***

After pulling her coat on, Susan stood in a short line to kiss Sara and Jim goodbye. The television flashed golf images across the screen while Grandma Irene, Elizabeth, and Dyane maneuvered towards the doorway to depart for lunch. Susan feared leaving Sara behind on a day she struggled to feel well and now realized her own lack of planning for days like this. She dropped her eyes in remorse before side-stepping towards her daughter. Susan felt Sara and Dyane's sisterly bond stretch between them until yearning covered Sara's face.

"Honey, may we bring you back something?" her mother asked.

Susan brushed Sara's cheek with tender cupping of her hand. Her heart ached as she witnessed Sara sitting bundled in the chair as her summer vacation began. Sara's eyes barely lifted up to her mother's. Susan didn't need a response to know what dimmed her daughter's face. Giving up an afternoon lunch with the women she loved took great courage, for which she had a current limited supply. Sara didn't deny her remaining physical limitations or setbacks but renounced them all the same.

Grandma Irene, Aunt Marie, Susan, and all three of her girls relished excursions to the grocery shop each week together and enjoyed lunch out every Thursday. Yet, in truth, they also took those moments for granted. As seasons changed, this moment with Sara served as Susan's clear reminder—a new one loomed on the horizon. Susan resisted her anxiousness and unmatched determination to exit. Her tastebuds screamed for a stir-fry pita or a club sandwich with mayonnaise, crispy french fries, a diet drink with no ice, and a full glass of ice on the side. It all waited for her at the pie serving restaurant, where everyone knew their names. Leslie, their favorite waitress, brought each drink, sometimes, even before they sat down at her assigned table. Lynette also tended to them well after asking about their family and Sara's health. That love and genuine concern for their family kept them coming back week after week.

Susan knew one thing. For Sara, missing this opportunity to join them compared to missing the next family party, not just a simple trip out to eat. So, her teen justified trying to hide her peaked disposition and disappointment from her without success. Family tradition or not, Sara exposed her fragility. Low white blood counts and rushes of toppling nausea kept her glued in place. Susan accepted the fact, if Sara ventured out, the risks and delays of another infection affected the next round of chemo the following week.

As far as she imagined, no one wanted Sara to feel normal again more than she did, whether possible or not. Susan looked about her, noticing Sara's flushed face and Dyane's pained expression near the foyer doorway. At that reminder, Susan forced herself to breathe through the anxiety and groaned instead. Her hope disintegrated. She fully blamed cancer for stealing this moment from her daughter and kissed Sara on the top of her head. She then pulled up her daughter's blanket and turned away from where she sat.

In silence, she retreated. The four women stepped out upon the porch, and Susan slammed the car door. She shook her head, hoping to dismiss the nagging feeling she forgot something important behind. Waiting for Dyane to settle in gave her an extra moment to clear her hazy vision. She felt pressure build inside her head and the beginning of a headache. From the front seat, she looked up towards the open front door, where no one stood. Her eyes searched her rearview mirror after swiping at them with the back of her hand. While descending the driveway, Jim appeared and waved;

then he closed the red entry door.

***

On June 2nd, Sara began the third round of chemotherapy. Contrary to the average patient response upon entering the hospital for chemo, Susan breathed some relief at her daughter's countenance. Sara strut down the corridor, with pillows wedged underneath one arm and an overnight bag, slung over the opposite shoulder, then leaned into her best friend, Lissa. The evening's first friend hospital sleepover energized the endless chatter between them. Susan considered Lissa's stay a much-needed help and blessing to herself. Surrounding many of Sara's chemotherapy treatments and emergency stays, Susan booked back-to-back hairdressing appointments to help with the increased expenses. Sara's renewed joy and thanksgiving that day also became the cheer to Susan's spirit.

In Susan's eyes, Sara's physician Dr. White continued to treat Sara with an intelligent disconnection and matter-of-fact countenance. His abrupt entrances and exits from Sara's room often lead her to consider his peculiar bedside approach. Because of it, Susan purposed to also observe the staff that tended her daughter. The same four or five nurses rotated on a daily and weekly basis, doing their jobs well but with the same kind of routine duty. Sara, unfamiliar with their professionalism, didn't notice. Up until now, this manner seemed to offer Sara's nurses protection, for they appeared unwilling to grow too close to the fragile children on the pediatric floor.

A nurse carried in a few chairs, unfolded the cold metal, and set one of them behind Grandma Irene.

"Oh, thank you, dear," she said.

Looking up, Susan kept moving. She hadn't considered it a sacrifice heading up to the hospital again, but her feet still ached from the long morning doing wash and sets for her regular customers. Sara's needs often became first priority. Susan overheard Dyane's breaths quicken and saw her eldest grasp around her widening abdomen. She then remembered Dyane expressing an aching pressure throughout her legs and a growing sense of imbalance after their long walk through the parking garage and corridors.

"Dyane, sit. *Sit.*" Her grandma stated.

"Dyane, please, sit," Susan said.

Dyane obeyed, placing her hand upon the arm of the recliner, bracing, and lowering herself onto the olive-hued vinyl. Her legs made a squeaking sound from sticking to the plastic just before sliding backward. Dyane embraced her belly with her hand again.

"I've got this; it's okay, you just take care of my grandbaby," she stated with a grin.

She felt the pull to rush home but stayed on task getting the girls settled in for the night. Susan threw her head back and laughed with Sara and Lissa as she passed out her strict overnight instructions. The time crunch to leave before rush hour drove her but not before she ran through the details upon her mind again. *Turn in the girls' breakfast order, empty Sara's bag into the cabinet, set up the toiletries in the bathroom, connect with the shift nurse, and review the girls' instructions.*

In many ways, Susan knew deep down Sara reflected her own temperament, but her boldness did not. Susan's shoulders tensed as Sara gave welcoming hugs to on-duty nurses; she herself didn't know. Irene squirmed in her seat, and Dyane picked up her purse on cue. However, before they shared goodbyes, Susan overheard Sara ask a nurse carrying a bag of fluid about her own low demeanor.

Sara perked up in her bed. Her eyebrows folded into a crease, and her head tilted. The nurse paused, wavering between a masquerade and transparency. Susan's neck began to sweat, and she felt an urgency to interrupt the long silence before the nurse's answer. Still, Sara pressed her for a genuine response. Susan recognized Sara only gave one option to the nurse in those moments—surrender. Susan witnessed the nurses' face softening to the sixteen-year-old lying in the bed with those captivating blue eyes. In love, somehow Sara persuaded her. The nurse's feelings about family began spilling from her lips. Susan also surrendered her discomfort, knowing it was just a matter of time before her daughter drew even more nurses out of their masked world and into her daughter's confessional. *Boyfriends, cheating, friendship, lies, parents, loss, grief*—she knew Sara longed to listen to it all because she broke for the hurting.

As their conversation slowed, Susan gathered her purse, her mother, and her pregnant daughter. She kissed Sara goodbye for the night, and then Lissa smiled and returned Susan's hug.

"By Mom G.," Lissa said.

Till That Day Comes

With a wave of her hand, Susan slipped past them all, praying the nurse found the comfort she sought.

Chapter 8

Strength Of Another Kind

Dyane drew in air until her lungs felt tight. Just before the pungent odor rose from the teal green bowl, she held her breath for as long as possible before letting it out. Dyane's fingertips brushed Sara's back while the surges of vomit jetted up again and again from her sister's stomach. Sara surrendered to the heaving. Underneath the cotton t-shirt, Dyane felt her sister's frail spine bending forward. Dyane's stomach churned also—adding to the queasiness of pregnancy. Sara lunged forward and arched toward the bowl again and again. Dyane fought the nausea that climbed up into her throat and created familiar squirts of saliva into the sides of her own mouth. Chemo played another nasty trick. In the process of healing, Sara faced horrific side effects. While some gaped, another ran for a paper towel to wipe the string of slime from Sara's mouth as she blew her nose.

Elizabeth returned home from her first year of college just

in time. Even at this moment, Dyane felt grateful. She passed the filled bowl off to her sister and it sloshed on the way to the bathroom toilet. Its contents flushed and Sara attempted a simple grin towards those standing nearby.

"Thank you," Sara said.

Dyane repositioned the tissue box on the table next to her. Then, Sara located her glasses and balanced them on the bridge of her nose. Dyane and her family drew close. In all of the upheaval, she and Elizabeth exchanged glances, speechless after Sara's spontaneous heaving.

***

The faded sun-bleached coils of Sara's hair fell away day by day, as did Dyane's hope of her sister's quick healing. Living in the same house, Dyane knew Sara's strands often entwined between her fingers or scattered her pillow in the morning. Her hairbrush also filled and slowed their parents' bathtub drain. Because Sara's hair grew thick and wavy—it went unnoticed at first, but Susan warned her daughter just the same.

"Sara, I will shave your head before I let you look patchy," her mother said.

Strength Of Another Kind

Susan's manner remained resolute and firm, but Sara's eyes widened and stared in surprise. Dyane picked up on Sara's fear. Not long before, Sara reflected identical alarm after discovering a thin patch upon her scalp while brushing her hair.

The day had come sooner than any of them had wanted. Susan and Dyane both bustled around in the basement beauty shop to help Sara face one of the biggest fears she avoided during months of chemo treatments. Dyane remembered the questions Sara posed to Dr. White at the beginning of her protocol, and they all revolved around the fear of her hair falling out. The conversation came flooding back into Dyane's head while the haircutting cape draped over Sara's shoulders and cascaded into her lap. Dyane set herself upon the wooden chair closest to the shampoo bowl and snapped a few photos of their moms intial shave.

After taking notice of Sara's melting demeanor, Dyane set the camera down with urgency. She rose and placed dry tissues within Sara's hand in exchange for the wet ones. Susan rubbed deep into Sara's back muscles to calm her sobs. Once she had, Sara twisted the shop chair enough to glance into the wall mirror beside her. She scowled. Appearing jarred, she angled her head to view its skin. Dyane's eyes

137

drooped, realizing nothing prepared her sister for a shaven scalp. She felt weak and sat again. None of them ready. Sara lived out another choice made for her, and she didn't like it. Her skin resembled the grey mood, and shadows framed her eyes. Then, those sparkling blue windows to Sara's heart captured Dyane's. They filled with tears and begged her big sister not to make light of the moment. Dyane's heart broke and her heart raced. She remained silent, considering her own reaction to having a head shaved, losing part of her own identity as a woman, and observing an important part of it lying on the linoleum.

Susan stood behind Sara and focused on the partially exposed scalp in front of her. She grimaced and looked up towards Dyane. Pain sat behind her eyes, begging for confidence. Then, she grasped the clippers and clicked them on—a steady loud hum filled the air. Their mom slid the shivering wide metal row of teeth up and over the curvature of Sara's head. With steadiness, she progressed a few inches at a time before tipping the long spirals onto the floor. Long brown nests sat tangled together underneath the chair, lifeless and still. While Sara's head hung forward, Dyane pressed the trigger upon the camera, documenting another momentous memory on their journey.

Sara's chin tilted enough for her and Dyane's eyes to connect again. Susan shut off the clipper motor and hung it back up on the hook behind the chair. The lighting reflected off of Sara's white head—now sprouting many goosebumps. With reluctance, Susan rotated her daughter upon the shop chair toward the mirror. It captured Sara's reflection, and she cried. While she buried her face into her hands, in an effort to get her mother's attention, Dyane made a weak attempt to form a subtle hand signal. Blocked from Sara's vision, Dyane's primitive message to Susan over Sara's wet face and sniffles somehow became clear.

Susan circled the chair. She bent forward and guided Sara's head into her chest, and fully embraced her baby girl. Palming a hand over Sara's ashen head, she held it tight for a long time. Both of them allowed their tears to fall. Dyane teared up also as she watched her mother's upper body tremble and listened to her soothing voice.

"I know, honey," she said.

Dyane set the camera back down, bit her stinging lip, and retreated upstairs towards the kitchen. Before long, Sara also emerged from the basement. Without a word and eyes downcast, she climbed an additional staircase toward her bedroom hideaway. Susan arrived soon after and set her drinking glass down on the counter with a heavy exhale. Dyane remained there for a moment—still. Her darting eyes tried to meet her mother's. She recognized the frozen look upon her mother's face—seeing it before many times while growing up. Unaware, Dyane felt like running for cover once again. She watched her mom lift the tumbler glass again with a shaky hand. Her lips pursed around the edge of the glass rim while Dyane observed the ice cubes slipping towards the mouth of the cup in a sea of red-flavored water.

Dyane grit her teeth a bit and ventured into a conversation.

"Are you okay?" she asked.

At the question, Susan's eyebrows moved closer together and wrinkled the area just above her nose.

"No. No, I'm not."

"I'm sorry, Mom. You look so angry," Dyane stated.

"Yes, I'm ticked. My head is pounding. I feel... I feel like I need to throw up—I didn't think it would bother me... I didn't know which would be worse, watching her hair fall out gradually or shaving her head bald. I guess, now I know."

Susan turned her back to Dyane, sniffed, and rubbed her collar bone. Dyane seized the opportunity to comfort her mother and hug her from behind.

"I have to be strong for her," Susan stated.

Dyane squeezed her mom tight. Looking back, clueless as a child and the oldest of three sisters, Dyane never knew the strength her mom held. In hindsight, Dyane misunderstood her determination. Her mom experienced marital traumas from her father Gerald, and she deserved much more respect and honor for that. They transformed her mother into the woman now battling before her eyes. Susan chose to reject the shame and stand up to the lies, the abuses, the fears, and allow God's strength to clothe her instead. She refused to hide the truth any longer from her family and friends. She refused a victim mindset. Quiet perseverance, wisdom, and faith in her dependable God gave her the unshakable confidence she needed to press on, even on this day. However, Susan needed reminding.

At this moment, Dyane accepted her mom's sorrow. They held each other tight until Dyane jumped back, feeling her unborn child flutter and kick. Giggling and wiping the tears from their eyes, they both placed their hands upon Dyane's quivering baby belly.

"Oh, my word!" Dyane exclaimed.

"That must've been a biggie! Honey, you should lay down for a bit while I make dinner," Susan stated.

Taking a deep breath, her mom smiled. She didn't dwell on her feelings for much longer and began to prepare the evening meal instead. Dyane shuffled down to her bedroom in obedience. As she laid there resting, many internal questions flowed in and out of her mind. *Will I ever have the same kind of courage, endurance, or perseverance my mom adopted in troubles? How will I react if my children face challenges to their health? What kind of example will I reflect to those around me when I'm struggling?* Every question formed a deeper twisting ache within Dyane's chest. It pushed deep, but she knew only one lasting solution remained—she prayed, and then she prayed some more. *God, please help.*

***

News of Sara's anxiety traveled at top speed amongst their family. As Dyane emerged from her bedroom and passed the wad of tangled hair in the downsta garbage can, she wondered if it would take months to grow back without chemo. Sara told Dyane about her hesitation to re-enter the hallways of her private high school days before. It meant people's stares, gossip, and whisperings about her appearance. Sara didn't want to become a freak show, standing out as the only one without hair. Yet, without her knowledge, the rumor of her hesitation spread.

"So, *what* happened?" Dyane asked.

Her mom laughed out loud, remembering the earlier evening event.

"The front doorbell rang while you were downstairs, and I answered it. You know, young David, our neighbor? Well, as soon as I opened the door, I see him and four of his buddies all standing there on our front porch with bald heads! Sara felt so embarrassed and wanted me to tell them that she couldn't come out. So, I told her—

'These guys *shaved their heads for you*—the least you can do is go talk with them.'

I think she was pretty cut to the heart because she did decide to go out there to meet them, and she's taking a long time coming back inside," Susan said.

At that moment, Dyane peeked around the corner through the storm door. She saw them all planted within the grass in the front yard, talking and laughing with each other. As they horsed around, Dyane considered their empathetic and loving gesture; one neighbor and four strangers—all shaving their heads for her sister. That secret act of kindness prompted her to wonder why her own courage and compassion wavered in doing it herself.

***

"Ooh, I like this! Thank you!" Sara exclaimed.

She squealed, pulling another new hat out of a floral gift bag. She tried it on, tipped her head with a smile, and looked into the dresser's mirror. Sara spun in place and pursed her lips like a serious model. Her fists rested upon her hips, and her upper body tipped into a curving formation. The next hat she pulled out looked creased from top to bottom until she popped it up into an umbrella of red, yellow, and white. Once she placed the white ring upon her head, all the ladies in her family gasped and snickered. As soon as the thin metal rods tilted upward into a primary-colored umbrella, they all agreed it looked beyond unusual. Sara's uncertainty in how to model it made the small crowd roar with laughter. Dyane envisioned her sister's loneliness if she ever wore the hideous thing out in public. Dyane held to her indecision over the hat's cute factor, like her stuffed dog Putter Paws. The hat had such a geriatric quality. An elderly man with black socks pulled up to his knees popped into Dyane's mind, and she snorted while she put it back in the yellow gift bag. Sara enveloped her head in one final hat made of purple fleece. Technically, it went on well until it swallowed her eyelids upon letting go of it. She lifted the fleece fabric enough to see and then pulled a side toggle cord. It gathered and puckered into a tight hole around Sara's face, leaving room for the tip of her nose and half of her upper lip to protrude out of it. Underneath the fabric, her muffled giggles lasted until Sara expanded the hole to take in a full breath and grin. As soon as she did, she grabbed her imaginary set of skiing poles and proceeded to swing them from left to right with her lanky arms. Dyane remembered their skiing lessons in Aspen, Colorado, with a giggle. Sara's playful laughter infected everyone watching her. After she slid off the hat, she waved her hands like fans in front of her flushed face and winked.

"Thank you, Aunt Marie," she said.

The ladies scurried around the room and hung the festive hats upon Sara's bedroom wall hooks. As the collection grew, Sara's eyes widened. They surrounded her in every color, shape, and style. Dyane empathized with Sara's relief, just as her sister's shoulders dropped and relaxed. Susan rubbed Sara's back and then squeezed her daughter's shoulders.

"It's amazing," Susan stated.

"Yes," Sara replied.

She smiled wide and reached for her closet doors. Opening them, she slid out a short-sleeved shirt to wear with jeans to school in the morning. She then held it up to match with a dark hat or two.

"That's a beautiful outfit, Sara," Dyane stated.

Grateful, Sara appeared not only happy but well-equipped and ready for any activity at school that came her way.

***

Sara enjoyed the hats and wore them every day to school, but she often commented on how much she missed having hair. It took some begging, pleading, and saving, but Sara nearly leaped in Susan's arms when her mom announced, after going out to lunch, they had an appointment at the wig shop.

A bell clamored upon their entry into the weathered brick storefront. The aged odor, shelved manikin heads, and an eerie silence all held Dyane's attention. As a group, they filed into a downtown establishment. In Dyane's guestimate—didn't see a lot of teenaged customers. The heads of hair roosted on foam head-forms, all brushed and shined with a synthetic, puffy appearance.

"Hey, Sara, how about a red wig?" Someone said from a distant corner.

Dyane imagined her sister in each color and stifled a laugh. A saleswoman greeted them, appearing eager to sell a dozen or more wigs to their crowd. Sara eyed a few styles while her mom discussed the natural wigs sold in the shop. After her guidance to a tall chair, Sara sat, took off her baseball cap, and waited to try on what she'd chosen—even with all of the comedic opportunities, time inched by. Some tried on wigs, lounged in beauty shop chairs, and a few sat on the dark, dated carpeting. With the final choices made, after hours of fittings and questions, Sara narrowed down her decision. She chose a very long, almost oversized, wavy wig with slight bangs plus a short sleek A-line-styled bob style, both similar to her natural color.

"Mom, I like them so much, thank you," Sara said. Just after closing the weighty glass door behind them, Sara smiled and hugged her mom tight before re-entering their car on Main Street.

***

Preparations for the days ahead required more courage than some felt ready to give. Dyane stood in the kitchen, her lips pressed around her upper and lower teeth tight until they disappeared. She scratched her head, wondering if she also needed to learn what the nurse instructed. Images of Sara needing the injections panicked her.

"You'll need to go and get an orange; its peel mimics the skin the best," stated Sara's nurse Maribeth.

Susan rifled through the refrigerator and gathered a few items from her kitchen. Elizabeth and Dyane followed her into her the family room, where Maribeth kneeled on the floor next to Sara's chair. Thankful for the willingness of the home health nurse to repeat her instructions on giving injections, Dyane still cringed. She didn't want to learn how to give them and definitely didn't want the practice. Her neck tightened. She then took a subtle step backward to bend it from side to side and crack it. Sara needed a series of four to five Neupogen injections after every weeklong chemo treatment. Elizabeth took her turn without hesitation after her mothers' successful first attempt. Orange juice spurted out from underneath the skin and into the air. Dyane jumped a bit after a few cool citrus droplets landed upon her skin. She watched their confidence with envy and shuddered at ever giving her baby sister an injection. The idea of administering the shot paled to the pressure and necessity she felt in keeping her alive with it.

"Here, Dyane, *your* turn," Maribeth stated.

Dyane shook her head. Intimidated by the nurse's instructions, she felt herself retreating into the background. Her shoulders dropped a little more with the release of her built-up apprehension. In her weakness, she prayed Sara never needed an injection on her watch.

***

It seemed as if each day brought about a new education. The morning bustled with activity at home. Everyone scurried around making breakfast while preparing for Maribeth,

Sara's favorite nurse, to arrive. With a perfect view, Sara watched with a bright countenance. Dyane retrieved a glass from the cabinet and filled it. Sara clutched her handful of morning pills. Tossing them a few at a time, she aimed them into the back of her throat and followed the mouthful with a wave of juice. After she swallowed the last one, she rubbed her stomach from side to side as if she had just eaten a large breakfast. Then, Sara's powerful burp blasted for everyone in the neighborhood to hear. Dyane laughed and shook her head.

"Excuse me!" Sara exclaimed.

"I should say so, girlfriend!" Dyane teased.

Sara sat in front of the sliding glass door and appeared eager for Maribeth's arrival. Later, at the sound of the doorbell, their little cousins Nichole and Brittany scurried to sit on the floor by Sara's chair. Maribeth entered the gathering with her usual smile and a warm chuckle. She hugged almost everyone and then squeezed Dyane tight.

"Hey, Dy," she greeted.

Then, Maribeth glanced over towards the soft green chair.

"Hey, Sar—you ready for this?"

After setting her bags on the floor next to the IV pole, Sara's petite nurse knelt upon the wood floor also. She then reached into her nursing bag and pulled out tubing, petroleum jelly, and connectors. Everyone stood in an almost perfect semi-circle, silent and still, listening to every instruction Maribeth gave.

"Sara, you're going to feed this in through your nose and swallow the Nasal Gastric or—NG tube down into your stomach. Then, Susan, you will fill this bag with the liquid meal replacement and then attach it to the feeding tube."

Susan nodded at the instruction.

"There cannot be any bubbles; you are going to have to fill the line and tap them out before finally attaching it," Maribeth said.

As the instructions continued, Dyane felt shocked by her mom's engagement. Her attention to detail, her teachability, her willingness to learn, and her remembrance of every one of Sara's needs impressed her. Dyane nodded, and she stood straighter as she observed Susan's courage. It grew, as did Dyane's respect for her mom, and she agreed with one reoccurring thought—*My mom is a rock.*

Till That Day Comes

Susan sat on the ottoman with a full cup of water and an inserted straw. The rest of them all stood around, ready for action and ready to do their part. A large bowl balanced on Sara's lap while Dyane drifted back to the reality of Maribeth's next question.

"Are you ready, Sara?" She asked.

Maribeth swiped the tip of the NG tube with petroleum jelly. Sara closed her eyes for a moment and then slid the plastic into her nose. Dyane held her breath—and the seconds ticked by. Just as it neared her throat, Sara shook her head, reached for the teal bowl, heaved, and threw up her lunch. The NG tube fell out of her nostril, and Maribeth grabbed the slippery plastic—wiping it off with a paper towel.

Dyane watched Sara's eyes close and the tipping of her head toward the chair back. Breathing deep, she lingered there and resisted attempting such a feat again. Sara's eyes opened with slow blinks; she raised her head and looked into the many expectant gazes upon her. Sara hesitated to begin again. Dyane also felt distracted and bit at the inside of her cheek. Dyane empathized with her pleading eyes of doubt and the pressure before her to learn something new in front of everyone. Even though Sara's nourishment depended

Strength Of Another Kind

on it, Dyane wondered if her mind searched for a way out of this—another alternative like the chemo options. While they waited for her to respond, it seemed to Dyane that an hourglass dripping black molasses took less time than those passing moments. Elizabeth stood near and held her crossed arms at the elbows. Dyane watched Maribeth plant herself in a new, more comfortable position on the floor. The nurse looked at Sara square in the eyes and nodded.

"Okay, Sara, are you ready to try again?" Maribeth asked.

It didn't seem to Dyane like Maribeth gave up, and her encouraging voice drew Sara into an eventual moment of consent. If her nurse believed, then so did Dyane. Because of her encouragement, along with Sara's full trust in her friend, Dyane clapped her hands quietly while Sara proceeded. Maribeth lubricated the tip again and picked up a water-filled glass in her other hand.

"Now, here, I want you to put the tube into your nose, like this—yes, and now at the same time, I want you to take sips of water, swallowing the tube down past your throat. Yes, that's right, you're doing great," Maribeth stated.

Her eyes widened with hope until Sara's eyes began to water and her face twisted. Gagging, Sara reached for the

153

bowl, pulled it close, and buried her face inside it. Dyane retreated less than a foot away. With loud repetitious groans and vomiting, the tube popped out of her nose again. Multiple times, they watched her lose her breakfast when the plastic reached the throat area. Sara's nose began to redden; she sniffed and then wiped at her eyes with a tissue. Until Sara spoke up in a scratchy voice, Dyane's mind paced between hope and fear.

"Lizzy—would you sing me the *Grand Canyon* song?" she asked.

Elizabeth didn't hesitate; she began the song just as Maribeth handed Sara the flexing tube. Sara's eyes fixed upon it as if staring it down into submission. Her widening eyes and grimaces fed the crowd's anticipation while she glided the tubing in again. As she sipped her glass of water from a straw, she began to swallow hard and fast with every word her sister sang. Just before it ended, Sara's words came out muffled.

"It's in," she said.

Squealing from her seat, Elizabeth squeezed Sara's arm, shaking it a bit. Dyane's bounced in place as her renewed optimism took root. Draped in cheers from around the room, the moment bore the fruit and victory they all prayed for. Elizabeth and Sara clutched each other in relief, and Sara's nurse laughed with awe.

"I've *never* seen anyone do it like that before," Maribeth stated.

Sara looked up over Elizabeth's shoulder. She smiled back at Maribeth from behind the long NG tube dangling from her nose. Dyane understood the non-verbal exchange; they both knew Sara's success depended upon Elizabeth's singing and her favorite nurse.

Chapter 9

Living Beyond A Wish

It grew cold in the Midwest, but that year brought with it Sara's long-anticipated break from treatments. Her weeks of preparation for Dyane's baby shower concluded with juggling multicolored balloons, an oversized Humpty-dumpty, and a surplus of baby gifts that didn't even fit into the one-bedroom her sister and brother-in-law resided in. Sara felt perky and buzzed around with loads of energy. The anticipation of her first nephew and touching Dyane's squirming belly gave Sara thrilling entertainment.

Not long after the baby shower, Sara arrived in the dining room for an important appointment with Sara's nurse Maribeth, Susan, and step-dad Jim. She pulled out a chair, sat, and wiggled upon it. The folder Maribeth pulled out of her large bag caused Sara to eke out a squeal. The cover said, "Make-A-Wish," and she placed it into Susan's hands. Jim's face appeared drawn and did not reflect the stirring of excitement Sara's did. Susan appeared ready to receive the packet, balanced an elbow on the table, then propped up her chin with a fist. Sara observed her mom flip the stapled pages to the left as Maribeth introduced the opportunity before them.

"Make-A-Wish fulfills trips for children with critical illnesses ages two and a half to eighteen years old. They offer hope for patients like Sara to lift their spirits and give them, as well as their families, renewed strength and hope to overcome the obstacles they are facing," Maribeth stated.

Jim sat back on his seat and sipped his ice water.

"So, Maribeth, what does a wish look like, and how much will this cost?" Jim asked.

"Well, Sara may choose the wish trip she goes on, and she can be as creative as she wants. Then, the Make-A-Wish team will create an unforgettable experience for her. It's meant to be a respite from all the stress for her as well as your family and is fully covered by Make-A-Wish," Maribeth stated.

After much discussion, ideas burst into Sara's mind about traveling to Alaska for her wish. However, the idea of traveling there in the winter got squashed by her mom and stepdad. Nevertheless, Sara's eyes glistened again.

"The Mall of America?" she asked.

The animated vision of shopping with more spending money than she ever imagined gave her a rush of elation. Her eyebrows raised, and the grin that spread across her face seemed very convincing to achieve what she hoped for. Sara welcomed fanciful visions of her shopping bags filled to the top. She envisioned herself at that moment, dressed in the latest fashions, with matching socks and hats for every outfit. She all but bounced where she sat. Before long, however, nudges of reality interrupted her dream. The joyous image of a stroll through the massive mall with bags dangling from her arms instead morphed into the certainty of her sitting in a wheelchair. Spinning wheels, dragging coats, and buried behind bags didn't sound fun to her at all. Sara drooped her head and felt deflated. She then shook a hand in the air.

"No, I can't handle the walking, and I don't need more stuff," she reasoned.

Those moments with her nurse passed more quickly than she intended under the pressure to make a choice. Before another suggestion was spoken, she shouted with finality—

"Hawaii!"

A perfect choice to so many in the winter months, she beamed at the revelation. In her mind, fresh gardenias draped about her neck, and warm sand trickled through her toes, just prior to stepping into the transparent aqua water. Sara nodded, exchanging excitable glances with her mom and stepdad over the table. They all swam in the awkward silence while Sara considered her lengthy flight from Chicago to Hawaii. Her nervous eyes searched the faces surrounding the table and rested on her mom before she made her next suggestion.

"You could quit smoking to survive the long flight?"

Susan's neck blotched and turned a shade pinker. Her obvious alarm to the suggestion spoke loud and clear.

"Now is not the time for me to quit—unless you want me to take up drinking—," she stated.

Also frustrated, Sara darted her eyes. Barbed words filtered through her teenaged mind. She adjusted her sitting position and bit the inside of her cheek. Silence helped her remember the last conversation between her parents about their smoking habit. Dyane understood. She remembered

Dyane's last overnight stay at the hospital with her when they spoke in whispers about feeling gypped. Sara felt irritated by the memory of her mom and Jim escaping to the hospital parking garage to smoke and leaving her alone in the room. She remembered the lost time with them and winced.

Sara sniffed, then blew her nose. She waited. As if frozen in the silence, Sara's mouth gaped. Deciding on a Make-A-Wish trip to Hawai—*Hawaii* stood still. *Mom, this is a once-in-a-lifetime chance to travel on an all-expense-paid trip to Hawaii! What's there to think about? C'mon! C'mon!* Sara thought as her heart beat faster, then she wiggled in her seat with nervous energy. Despite the flight length, she knew by their own silence; they took the suggestion into serious consideration. They reviewed their wall calendar, counting the last few months of the year, discussing Christmas plans and Dyane's January 11th due date. By the time they discussed at length Jim's available vacation days and Sara's break from chemo, Sara bounced her leg. The stillness seemed to last longer than her patience allowed. Her eyebrows slanted, and her fingers intertwined in suspense.

"Okay," they said.

Sara leaped to her feet as if she burst like a cork from a

shaken bottle. Into their arms, she fell squeezing, screaming, and swaying. Jim and Susan laughed at her flow of energy which then prompted Sara to dance in place and clap her hands.

Later that evening, after announcing the news of the Hawaii trip, panic swept over Dyane's face.

"January, you guys are going on your trip through the first week of January?" she asked.

The pitch of Dyane's voice raised, and her mouth fell open a little. She straightened her glasses and twisted her fingers through her hair, and gripped it.

"Honey, we are so sorry. It's our only option," Susan stated.

Sara's heart began to race as she searched Dyane's face and heard the discouragement shaking her voice. *No, no, no*—she thought in panic. She didn't want her sister to feel sad but wanted to make everything better, and rested her hand on Dyane's arm. She did want to include Dyane and Joseph like they all originally planned and now wondered to herself about the possibility of waiting a few more weeks to begin the next treatment.

"The cruise line won't allow you to travel so near to your due date Dy and we need to fit this trip in around chemo, Jimmy's vacation time, and your delivery as best as we can. We are so sorry. Let's just pray you don't go into labor while we're gone," Susan stated.

"But what if you guys aren't back in time?" Dyane asked.

Sara wondered the same thing, wondered if she made a mistake, and listened to her mom's reassurance over the valid question. The travels across the Pacific Ocean, plus the length of time, made Sara's stomach flip-flop. The image of the emptier house over Christmas break and a week into the new year left Sara empathizing with Dyane's disappointment. It also prompted her to continue problem-solving and notice her mom's steadiness.

Conversations over the details drew out until Dyane excused and lifted herself to go to the bathroom. Sara lifted her head. Dyane attempted to reassure her little sister with a soft smile and a pat on her shoulder, but it didn't convince Sara.

"Don't worry about us; we'll wait for you. But, don't have too much fun without us," Dyane said.

Dyane winked, but Sara nodded thin-lipped and looked

away. She empathized with Dyane's nervousness, her stifled feelings, and the missed opportunity. Sara also knew if she didn't go on her Make-A-Wish trip, she might never have the chance again.

***

As the trip drew nearer, Sara bubbled with elation and bounced on her toes while speaking with her nurse friends about the anticipated Hawaiian adventure. Dr. White listened to Sara with great attentiveness one day as he checked her over at the hospital. Just as Sara finished a lively description of her tropical escape—he finished his exam and grasped his stethoscope upon his lap.

Dr. White folded his instrument in half before repositioning and stared into Sara's eyes. Sara's smile weakened, however, under the weight of his firm instruction and bounced the scope upon his lap.

"*No* parasailing, and *no* swimming with the dolphins," he stated.

Sara's eyes began to blink rapidly. She failed to contain herself or the shrill pleading that spilled from her lips—

"Please, please, *pleeeease!*" She cried.

He tapped the stethoscope upon his lap again and gave his greyed head an emphatic shake.

"*No, no, no,*" he stated.

Sara swallowed hard, and her shoulders raised and tightened. Regardless of Sara's looks of horror, displeasure, or pouts—the possibilities of swaying Dr. White appeared nil. He rose. Silent and resolute, he strolled out of her private room, but Sara called out to him with the last word—

"You're a jack—" Sara said.

Sara saw her mom's body flinch out of the corner of her eye, her head whip around, and her voice screech—

"*Sara!*"

To Sara, her argument almost seemed innocent, and she deflected the blame.

"What? It's in the Bible," she stated.

Her mother's eyes rolled, and then Sara swallowed hard. She fastened her sight on Dr. White's grey blazer, readjusted her sheet, grinned sheepishly, and cleared a drying throat. His slight pivot, without reply, made Sara's stomach drop and her feet tingle. He continued his exit, but not before Sara caught a snicker cross his face.

***

On an icy January day, Sara handed her stepdad her last bag. Suitcases collected by the frost-bitten front door waited. While Jim began to load the line of suitcases and duffel bags into the car, Sara noticed his nostrils flare. She knew he despised going to O'Hare Airport. Plus, she remembered his comments the night before about money, all he left behind for his assistant at work, her own medical risks while away, and knew deep down, he desired one more cigarette before leaving. He grew quiet before gathering the next batch of bags to load into the trunk. In turn, she avoided his eyes and sat down on the barstool.

Once loaded, Sara spoke to Dyane's oversized baby-belly in the foyer.

"Now, don't come until I get back," she stated.

A ripple of movement responded to her touch and instructive words.

"Prayerfully, the baby won't. I don't know what I would do without any of you! Love you, sis, love you, Liz," said Dyane.

Dyane returned their squeezes in an awkward bend forward before everyone stepped onto the front porch.

"Bye Mom, bye Jimmy—please have fun, take lots of pictures! *Do not stress, relax you two!*"

Sara pulled her fleece hat over her head and cinched it while she waited. She shook her head at her mom and stepdad's obvious restlessness and smiled big. The friction under her rubbing hands warmed her while Dyane shoved her own into the pockets of her overalls. The billows and swirls of vehicle exhaust dissipated into the winter air as they all neared the car. The crisp dull day in the northern Illinois suburb hung over them like a canopy.

"Bye! Love you! Love you!" Dyane yelled.

Sara then held up her hand and returned her silent hand signs for, "I love you, bunches."

In true family fashion, her grandparents, Dyane, and Joseph all waved goodbye from the front stoop until they disappeared from the *cul-de-sac*.

Sara tipped her head upon the headrest and closed her eyes. She felt happy imagining their Hawaiian trip—the blue waters, the snorkeling, the soft sand, the waves, the sunsets, and the tropical plumeria perfuming the air as Dyane described to her.

"How are you doing back there, Sara?" Susan asked.

Sara opened her glowing eyes. She felt warmth radiate throughout her body from the adrenaline and spoke with an unrestrained smile—

"Awesome, awesome, *awesome*."

***

Sara's mouth gaped. In port, delighted and distracted by the monstrous ship and the lapping aquamarine water surrounding it, she stood speechless. Not only did the island hopper cruise ship greet them with elegance, but palm trees waved their oversized leaves in a festive welcome. Then, crowds of stylish tourists walked past and up the ramp where Hawaiian greeters waited.

After draping soft white gardenia and plumeria leis about

their necks, the islanders also placed a kiss upon their cheeks. Sara's smile expanded at the tropical welcome to paradise. The fragrance of soft and delicate flowers intoxicated her, transporting Sara to a much-needed restful and dreamlike place. Then the warm wind danced around her legs and painted toes.

As they set sail, the vast sparkling ocean offered a visual reminder of the distance between them, home, work, and Sara's ever-increasing medical needs and responsibilities. At first sight of the aquamarine coast from the ship, Sara witnessed her mom, Jim, and Elizabeth focus their stare at the coastline. They stood silent. Jim appeared to loosen and tuck a thumb around a beltloop as his arm embraced Susan around the waist. She rested her head upon his chest and closed her eyes. Breezes caressed Sara's head and blew Elizabeth's blonde hair into the sky. Sara released the last of her own tension into the wind. With a clear head, she glanced around and found a few deck chairs. Hobbling over, she fell into one. As the water swooshed by, she planted her feet upon a rail and let her bare legs soak in the sunshine. Leaning her head back and holding a floppy white hat, she considered every shape of the clouds, then expanded her lungs with the kind of peace only humid salty air carried.

Till That Day Comes

The winding, crowded line to the ship's glossy excursion counter felt daunting to Sara, but she remained committed to her mission. Elizabeth fidgeted with her excursion pass. Sara remembered what her mom and Jimmy warned them about before leaving the cabin. She did remember what Dr. White said, but she felt conflicted. Sara's teenaged mind considered the once-in-a-lifetime opportunity and as she inched closer to the counter to peruse the posted excursion list. She caught sight of Elizabeth's nervous pass bending and Sara made up her mind. Since their parents allowed them to go alone and choose the adventure they wanted most, they did. Sara exhaled a soft whistle after she signed the excursion form. After paying the extra fees on her parent's cruise tab. Elizabeth leaned over her shoulder before Sara spun around. The adrenaline rush down to her fingertips still pulsed through her body. The frozen look on Elizabeth's face almost forced her to ask for the form back, but Sara instead decided to wrap her arm through Elizabeth's and pull her forward toward the gift shop.

***

Before she knew it, Sara felt an unfamiliar twisting inside

her stomach after she stepped onto the boat's platform with Elizabeth close behind. The damp air blew droplets over her naked scalp as the rising navy water lapped at the speed-boat's side. Sara watched Elizabeth's distress build. Tan hands buckled her sister into the harness, and Sara snorted a slight giggle. Sara then turned her focus upon reading the lips of her bronze instructor, to whom she flashed a smile at once as he tightened all of her safety clasps.

"When you are ready, just give us a thumb up, 'kay?" He asked.

Both Sara and Elizabeth nodded—one with *much* more enthusiasm than the other. The engine began to hum a loud reverberation, and Sara turned her head at the moment she thought she heard her name. With her face scrunched, eyes squinting, and her hands swiping blonde tangling strands out of her face, Elizabeth yelled toward her sister into the wind—

"I'm scared out of my mind!"

Sara's head tipped backward in a fit of naughty laughter.

"Hey, if I'm going to die anyway—" Sara stated.

At that, she gave an emphatic thumbs up to the driver. Her voice trailed behind her as the boat yanked their harnesses and picked up its speed. Elizabeth's throat screeched while pleading her own case one last time—

"Wait! But what about me?" Elizabeth cried.

Their bodies lurched forward and propelled upward towards the cloud above them. On their first excursion, Sara successfully disobeyed Dr. White's stern instruction. Life vests, ropes, and seagulls kept them company high above the white-capped ocean. They flew against the air currents and swung behind the small speck of a boat. Sara looked downward at her view. She noticed half-naked ants dotting along the shoreline. The girls sailed beside each other smiling, and their eyes continued to squint and water until Elizabeth reached out a flailing arm. Sara blocked the wind from her face and gave her wide-eyed sister the attention she cried for.

"What if they dip us into the water and sharks bite our feet?"

Sara threw her head back and screamed into the air as loud as possible, so the sharks below left them alone. The beauty and the exhilarating ascension toward all the blueness appeared to convince Elizabeth to let go of her worries and succumb to the joyful moment at hand. In a blink, shouts and laughter revealed a complete surrender within them both. Sara and Elizabeth both glided through the air warmed by sunlight, cooled by the breeze, and awed by the creation surrounding them.

Another soft gust whipped Elizabeth's lengthy hair around her face as soon as she stepped off of the boat ramp and onto the pier. Sara topped her head with a white floppy hat and slung her beach bag over a rosy shoulder. After an hour on the speedboat, their steps back into the sand felt shaky. Sara unfolded her sunglasses, placed them upon her nose, and peered down the coast from end to end. She enjoyed the glitter of the ocean and all the rainbow of umbrellas facing it. Sara and Elizabeth dropped onto their beach towels, laughing—grateful and relieved by the warm earth below their shivering bodies.

They delighted in the Hawaiian theme of hanging loose and did just that until Susan and Jim arrived. While the teens waited and buried their feet within the sand, people shuffled and strolled in front of their towels along the water's edge. Men and women of all shapes and sizes, from so many different places, laid underneath the sun to bake. Sara glanced around her. She struggled to hear the people laughing at the bar with their umbrella embellished fruit drinks. Sara wrapped her dry shoulders with a white cover-up and slipped her arms inside with Elizabeth's help. Elizabeth then settled in and leaned back against her rolled-up beach towel. Sara watched the waves crash in. At the moment, more people passed by them, appearing distant to her. Sara realized how detached she felt from the situation she sat in as well. She peered at her sister next to her, resting on the hot pink towel, and then glanced up and down the beach at those within her line of sight. Sara's neck grew hotter, and she struggled to manage the feelings that churned inside. She tapped her feet upon the sand over and over again, allowing the grains to flow between her toes. Acknowledging her body housed a terminal illness felt right in the moment somehow. She knew few beachcombers understood, but rather than stifle her feelings any longer, she confessed them to her sister. Sara sifted the sand between her fingers.

"Elizabeth, we've become so consumed with cancer, ya know? Yet these people go about their lives as if it'll last forever, but we know firsthand it won't. My heart aches for them; I want them to know this is all so temporary. I want them to know God sees them and loves them as they are. I feel like I just want to shake them and say—'wake up, wake up, stop living just for yourselves. You aren't promised tomorrow! God has a plan for your life and a future filled with eternal hope if you'll just seek Him and receive what you truly need—Jesus Christ, His Son.'"

Chapter 10

Day Dreaming

Sara observed her mom Susan glance at the wall clock again and then over to Jimmy. He stood next to her, rocking from one foot to another in the waiting room—struggling to find a comfortable standing position. Elizabeth shifted herself on the upholstered seat while looking at a women's magazine, and Sara sat beside her upon the couch in an abnormal silence. Sara tilted her head taking notice of the painted pastel walls enveloping her. Framed nursery rhymes hung tight against them, and at that moment—a thought wisped through her mind.

You'll never be able to have children, it said.

Sara's eyes watered. Her mind wrestled over the words, allowing them to roll around in her head while babies cried from the birthing rooms nearby. She sighed, hung her head, and closed her lids. She fought to guard her mind. During the long wait, her thoughts shifted between praying for Joseph and Dyane's baby's safe delivery and images of what the future might also hold for her.

"It's a boy!" a voice exclaimed.

It rang out to everyone, desperate for an answer. Clustering together, their family inched through the birthing room doorway, tiptoeing up to Dyane's bedside, where Joseph stood holding his wife's hand. He smiled as a proud daddy should, and Dyane sighed deep as she looked toward her first visitors. Her big sister then tilted their beautiful new son, Cullen, towards Joseph's parents Lawrence and Kathleen, as well as towards their own, Elizabeth, and herself. A weak, hushed voice escaped Dyane's lips as she wiped at her cheeks with the back of her fingers in lieu of a tissue.

"You're aunties—" she said.

Sara and Elizabeth both drew near to her bedside. Sara felt cautious of making a wrong move by her wide-eyed nephew. Dyane tipped him up again, slipping down the swaddling blanket underneath his little chin. His navy blue eyes widened and gazed at their shadows.

"*Aww*—" they said together.

Their chiming voices brightened Dyane's smile and relieved the last bits of tension Sara held in her muscles over the last thirteen and a half hours of her sister's labor. As they nestled Cullen into the crook of her arm for the first time, she felt grateful. Sara cherished these moments as the best gift of all compared to Christmas and her Make-A-Wish trip. Answered prayers assured Sara God valued the whole birth event, and He wanted her at the hospital to hold her first nephew on January 11th. For the first time, as she wrapped Cullen's tiny fingers around her own and observed his trust, she realized God also took care of her. He cared about what she cared about and trusting Him fully mattered more than she ever comprehended before.

***

In February, Sara's hand wrote a new update letter to her school. She drafted the letter three times before her grandma typed it, and then they sent it off for sharing with her class-mates.

Dear friends at Illiana Christian High School,

I wanted to let you in on how I have been doing. You, having never experienced cancer, do not know what it is like. Hopefully, you will never have to. I'm not going to say it is a wonderful experience, but I've learned a lot about myself, life, and how my body works. It's frustrating not to be able to run around with the energy I used to have. I don't feel comfortable talking as openly as before. I've learned to be strong, to never give up, and I have learned to give everything to Christ.

After two surgeries, six chemo treatments, celebrity visits from a Bears quarterback, a Blackhawks player, and a Hawaiian cruise later, I'm hopefully going to be able to come back to school and finish my sophomore year with you. I pray I will be able to graduate with my senior class.

I'm sixteen but don't get to enjoy what sixteen-year-olds do. I often feel alone. A normal sixteen-year-old has things to do, guys or girls to date, and has to finish schoolwork that was due three days earlier. Before cancer, that was big stuff. Right now, I have to concentrate on getting better and keeping my weight up. I never thought I'd hear myself say that. Hopefully, in the future, wondering if a guy likes me will be my biggest problem.

Cancer is not just found in older people but in a wide variety of ages. I never thought it could happen to me, but it did. I know God didn't give me this cancer; He only allowed it to happen. He will walk me through this. I don't want to be recognized as just the girl with cancer but a child of God.

I want to thank all of you for all of your prayers, Illiana. You've been so supportive. Everyone has helped me to never, never, never give up.

As a word of advice, "Live life like you'll die tomorrow, die knowing you'll live forever."

Love In Christ,

Sara Schreck

***

Identifying with Dyane in a new way, Sara better understood the commonality they both shared. Sara watched her sister's recovery process with interest. With stitches to heal from, Dyane moved slow. Her healing took a few weeks, as did the adjustment to the new life of motherhood. Sara now understood what it felt like to provide assistance rather than just receive it. Sara helped Dyane walk down the steps and offered to retrieve things like diapers, wipes, and burp clothes for her.

In the mornings, Sara often inched downstairs to visit Cullen while still dressed in her loose flannel jammies.

"Where's my little baby boy?" She'd call.

Curled up on the couch in the basement family room, Sara returned Dyane's smile as she finished nursing him. Then, after swaddling her drowsy nephew, the love of her life received a slathering of his auntie's good morning kisses. Sara cooed gentle words to Cullen.

"Hi…" she said.

Sara readily took on the task of morning diaper changing, if asked, with a smile upon her face. While Sara hoped to carry her nephew to the changing table, Dyane often hesitated. Neuropathy numbed Sara's hands and feet more every day, and Dyane questioned if she felt steady enough to carry Cullen so early in the morning. If Sara felt confident, Dyane set her son into his auntie's cradling arms. After walking side by side towards the bedroom, Sara unwrapped her nephew upon the padded table. Sometimes, Cullen cried and shivered, and Sara sang a little lullaby to console him. She stared at his tears and watched his little breaths. He, in turn, if he calmed, studied her silhouette against the back of their grandma's peach-colored window shade. Sara felt Dyane watching them both from afar, beaming with affection.

Making her way with Cullen back to the family room, Sara snuggled him while Dyane tended to breakfast, a shower, and switching loads of laundry. Her long fingers trailed over Cullen's soft white face, traced his chin, and then her hand slid over his downy hair. Her heart ached. She remembered she might not give birth to children herself, but knew Cullen represented more than a nephew to her. Sara clung to every moment with subtle desperation—every smile, every burp, as if to soak them deep into her soul. Aware of her maternal longings, she found increasing grace and satisfaction through Cullen somehow. She cherished those seconds, minutes, and hours together. Knowing for a fact that only a capable, loving Father orchestrated those moments together after having once lived so far apart.

It almost seemed ironic to Sara as she thought back over the month before. She never imagined her sister and husband residing in their grandma's bedroom that sat underneath her own. Sara knew their dreams to re-enter ministry waited while their newborn rocked in the handmade cradle beside the bed. More-Poppo's creation held his first great-grandson, and she hoped for it to somehow hold hers as well. Sara realized the proverb true, that no matter how many temporal plans a person makes it's God who guides every step. Nestling into her grandmother's chair and rocking Cullen, she felt grateful God's steps led them home to her. Sharing in these joy-filled moments with this precious new life blessed her in ways only God knew she needed for such a time as this.

***

A new week brought with it a wild mix of feelings for Sara. For her, an unexpected storm built on the horizon. This new season rolled and churned, increasing in speed moment by moment. The announcement of Elizabeth's wedding engagement took Sara by surprise and prompted her to act. She felt compelled to speak to her sister Elizabeth honestly. Sara didn't withhold her feelings of jealousy or her fears. She also confessed her irritation and frustration over the blooming relationship between her sister and Neil. She knew none of it caught Elizabeth by surprise, though. During more recent chemotherapy treatments, Sara struggled with severe mood swings, moments of depression, insomnia, and additional irritation with her doctors. The moment Elizabeth announced her engagement, Sara didn't feel like her true self. Uninhibited, her face grew hot every time she thought about Elizabeth leaving, and she shared her opinion whenever she had the chance. The long stretch of chemical pumping appointments and all their side effects robbed Sara of any joyful news. Even though she suspected the engagement, she sulked and complained anyway.

In reality, life itself continued for her family even as she faced the largest battle of her life, and it rattled her. At times, pivotal moments like the engagement triggered feelings of abandonment, which left her also feeling forgotten and simply left behind altogether.

Sitting in her room one evening, Sara revisited a letter Dyane had written to her and felt her face warm.

"Dear Sara,

I am sleeping in your room tonight. I keep finding sponge-tooth brushes in the bed, though! Do you sleep with those? I stole a piece of stationery; I knew you would be very thrilled about that. I hope and pray you are continuing strongly with your devotion time and prayer time—I will continue to pray for you in that area. You know, Satan, the great deceiver, can make bad things seem good—like maybe time you spend on other things at the hospital or running around with friends when you're home. They can be used as a distraction at times to keep you from drawing closer to God. Something to think about if you may not be having a solid, quiet time each day. I love you and think of you often. I don't like to talk on the phone because I don't feel like I'm getting a good picture of what's going on with you . . ."

At that, she placed the letter on her nightstand and clutched Putter Paws to her chest. She knew God used Dyane to intervene. She adopted her sister's advice, grabbed her prayer journal off the bookshelf, and admitted her infuriating jealousy. She accepted her responsibility. In order to preserve Elizabeth's and her relationship, she needed a designated time to pray things through. Second, she needed more wisdom before beginning to work things out with Elizabeth. Sara admitted to sole craving focus upon her feelings. As she wrote her prayers, she swallowed hard. Knowing sharing attention with her older sister Elizabeth over her wedding plans stirred up more emotion than she wanted to admit to herself or anyone else. Letting go of this immaturity, self-centered thinking, and fear took a huge leap of faith. She slid her palm down the length of her face as she considered the next steps. Then she remembered when Dyane and Joseph moved in, and Cullen arrived. Sharing and trust took practice, as did letting Elizabeth go. With that in mind, after a prayer time and before her emotions got the better of her, she grabbed stationery out of her top dresser drawer.

Penning a letter before her sister's July wedding, felt right and the words began to flow, encompassing everything she should have said at first.

Dear Elizabeth,

It's so hard to say goodbye. Even though it's not going to be forever, I'm going to miss you a lot. We've become so close the past year, and I'll cherish the memories that we've had.

I don't know how to express how much I care for you. I've had a lot of friends come and go, but our friendship will be forever.

I really think you are a blessed person to have Neil. You two are made for each other. Don't forget to write and call, and most of all come visit me in the hospital. It's going to be tough without seeing you. It's going to be tough without seeing your smiling face to brighten my day over in that place they call a hospital. I love you, Elizabeth, ☺ God bless you always!

Love in sisters always!

Sara ☺

P.S. I love you, Neil. Please take good care of her for me. And go gentle on her too. ☺

Sara came to her senses and brought relief to the unspoken tension surrounding the wedding. She cringed, knowing she had to give up much to gain perspective and maturity over her sister's engagement. Sara's improved opinions of Neil became clearer as the summer progressed, and before long, she gushed.

"Lizzy, he's got muscles, and he's so *sweet*. He's the full package," she stated.

Sara knew deep within her soul, she felt grateful for Elizabeth's choice. Impressed by God's work, she admitted to liking the idea of calling both brother-in-law's *pastor*. She now realized more than anyone the quality men God brought into both sisters' lives through their church. While far from perfect, she observed both growing in their personal relationships with God. Peace filled her. Sara knew Elizabeth's redheaded wrestler loved, cherished, and prepared to commit to her for a lifetime. Leading well already, she understood why

Elizabeth thought he might one day lead his own church. Even though Sara knew her sister felt unqualified to take on the role of a pastor's wife, she, instead, felt confident. Elizabeth's readiness to glide down the aisle as his bride and stand as the helpmeet by his side, confirmed it.

***

Following the very first CT scan of the year, Sara set her mind on one thing on the ride home. She wanted to grow hair for Elizabeth's July wedding ceremony. The image of curling it excited her, as did the idea of sporting a few sun-streaked highlights. Determined to pause chemotherapy with all its nasty side effects, she rested in peace over her independent and adult decision.

Of course, after the *announcement, not everyone in her family agreed she made the* right one. She didn't expect it. Even Dyane's maternal viewpoint and her big sister's opinions kicked in.

"I honestly don't think it's the best idea, Sar—. What if the lesions on your liver multiply or spread throughout your body during the summer?" Dyane questioned.

Sara straightened her back and searched her big sister's eyes.

"I understand you feel alarmed, Dyane, maybe even afraid, but I've thought a lot about it and prayed about this a lot, like longer than everyone else has," Sara stated.

Everyone asked questions of her. *What if...what if...what if.* Sara didn't know. She just knew she didn't want to feel sick at Elizabeth's wedding or strut around bald, wearing her evergreen maid-of-honor dress.

In the midst of it all, she felt herself changing, almost like an unfolding butterfly. She also felt alive like never before, with God-given courage to make such a huge decision on her own. Throwing off her insecurities, she didn't feel like the same cheerleader that got cancer more than a year ago. Sara now drew on God's comfort whenever she felt overwhelmed. She also sought His wisdom whenever she didn't know what to do. She prayed about every single thing. She didn't just say she believed in God; Sara started acting in faith on whatever she sensed Him leading her to.

Sara asked people she trusted to pray for and with her. If anything, she became sensitive to everyone else's uncertainty. Did she believe in God's ability to extend grace by keeping the legions from spreading before the wedding? Sara did, however, deep down, she cowered at taking these steps of faith alone and longed for someone willing to go on every twist and turn with her. Dyane struggled with Sara's new confidence, and it appeared regardless of her elder age, she didn't know what to do. *Am I wrong to feel discouraged or need Dyane's help? Where is Dyane's courage?* Sara wondered.

Sara remembered Dyane's favorite Bible verses in

Isaiah 40:30-31, for they guided her sister many times.

Even youths grow tired and weary, and young men stumble and fall; but those who hope in the LORD will renew their strength. They will soar on wings like eagles; they will run and not grow weary; they will walk and not be faint.

At that moment, Sara knew she must pray for hope, pray for her big sister, and for God's perspective on this. She needed strength and clarity. Sara thought she knew best, or maybe Dyane, but something in her gut reminded her, only God did.

***

As they dove into the summer months, Sara continued to make the most of the weeks she hovered on hold between her chemo treatments. She grabbed her bathing suit and packed the appropriate work clothes before jumping onto a plane and traveling back to Arizona. Visiting her father and working in his office stretched her with responsibility and put spending money into her wallet. Following her trip, Sara enrolled in a driver's education class and enjoyed her sense of accomplishment. Dyane fully supported her but did confess to fears over Sara's diminishing reaction time behind the wheel. Just the thought of Sara in the driver's seat of a car—had the potential to create Dyane's first grey hair.

Dyane and her husband Joseph now lived only fifteen minutes away, but in this busy season of Sara's life, it felt like they had moved much farther. Great comfort arrived at Elizabeth's return from college to spend time with her before marrying Neil. Elizabeth shared the same ecstatic feelings. The hours they poured over bridal magazines and made plans for Elizabeth's wedding made the weeks and months flee by.

Sara joined her mom in the kitchen while she patted meatloaf together one evening and cringed. Susan chattered on with Dyane about her own recent experiment with tanning lotion before the bridesmaid dress fitting. Smirking at Sara while she put the loaf pan in the oven, she shared about nurse Maribeth's visits and how they became even better friends.

Day Dreaming

Sara couldn't help but giggle as her mother came close to hyperventilation with laughter over their recent debacle, and Dyane hopped with eagerness to hear more about it.

"Sara made dinner for Maribeth last night. Then the next thing I know, Sara's dragging her to the upstairs bathroom. I'm still unsure what happened, but after peeking into the bathroom, I ran and got my camera," Susan stated.

"Sara stood by Maribeth as she sat balanced on top of the counter. With her legs outstretched, Sara applied sunless tanning lotion to Maribeth's legs," she said.

"I came into the bathroom as Sara gave Maribeth an explicit list of instructions, all while her own lotion-filled hands turned bronze in the process. Her giggles echoed, bouncing off the tile while Maribeth tried to compose herself on top of the bathroom counter. I even had to turn my hearing aides down! Sara attempted to steady her before Maribeth's feet hit the floor. Then, picture them wobbling onto their feet and looking down at Maribeth's legs, then Sara's hands. They literally turned a golden orange before their very eyes," Susan said.

Sara blushed and shook her head as the story made Dyane burst out in laughter. Shrugging her shoulders, she smiled, grateful Dyane appeared proud of her creativity.

***

Looking into the full-length mirror, grandma sat on her knees, pinning the bridesmaid dress to fit. Sara grinned and admired the beauty of her gown. Lace gathered off of her shoulders, emphasizing Sara's petite frame. Sara's hair grew, and rather than coming in dark blond and spiral curled, it came in medium blonde and straight. Her cute short hair, a spunky pixie style, fit her own personality. Sara looked up into the mirror for a brief moment, and then she squirmed a little. With pins pinched between her grandmother's lips, she tilted her head up and scolded Sara with a muffled but playful voice.

"Now Sara, would you *please* stand still?" she asked.

Grandma Irene made every formal dress for her granddaughters for as long as Sara remembered. The purring of her sewing machine continued to comfort Sara, even at the age of seventeen. Irene created each of their dresses for special school events, dances, and not to mention Dyane's own wedding. Sara remembered her grandma allowing Dyane to take a dress pattern and redesign it for her to sew. Irene often listened to Dyane chatter on with all of her design ideas, and then—she'd release a long breath she held in.

"*Okay*...let me see what I can come up with," she'd say.

Her grandmother held back any complaints. She always encouraged creativity, even if it cost her the extra time, money, and patience to modify it.

***

On July 30th, the summer sun rose with hope, joy, and a lifetime covenant waiting for the bride and groom to solidify. Both Elizabeth and Neil made their final preparations in different locations. Sara's hair became the perfect length for styling, and to those she didn't know, she appeared healthy rather than sick with cancer. Sara and Dyane both felt a slight burden of responsibility to make sure their father, from Arizona, felt welcome and included among so many estranged family members, friends, and strangers. As his peace waned, though, he became more silent and distant. The weight of his need grew throughout the day like a towering shadow that lurked in the room. Sara empathized and acknowledged her own distraction at the beautiful marriage ceremony.

Elizabeth and Neil chose an early reception, as Dyane and Joseph did a few years before. Sara understood their hope to avoid their father's problematic issue with alcohol at the receptions and make things more affordable for him. Sara wondered what kind of reception she'd plan for her wedding. She imagined the yellow calla lilies, the music, the gathering of friends and family, and her pastors declaring her love for her husband. Her smile softened as she took another sip of her sparkling grape juice and remembered her sisters' disappointment, though. They forwent the kind of reception that allowed a first dance by candlelight. That's what she wanted, but their dad's addiction cost each of his daughters on their wedding days. She tossed buttermints and peanuts into her mouth and crunched them slowly. As she glanced around the bright hall they ate in, their loss grieved her.

At the moment, Sara also wondered if she'd forgo dancing at her own wedding. She doubted it. Instead, Sara daydreamed. She imagined herself wrapped in white, dancing without a care in the world and filled with joy, surrounded by music minus the suffering. She envisioned the most beautiful bride with a complete focus upon her groom—an unforgettable and glorious day.

Chapter 11

Stark Realities

Three days followed Elizabeth's and Neil's wedding day, with the dry-cleaned wedding gown packed away and the green maid of honor dresses hung with care in the back of the guest room closet. Dyane breathed a sigh of relief after helping her mom put her home back together. Elizabeth now enjoyed her honeymoon in Tennessee, and Sara seemed more reflective than usual at home. Dyane noticed the wedding letdown appeared to hit Sara hard. A stark reality resurfaced again in her own mind—cancer refused to stand in a corner and wait any longer. She believed the renewal of Sara's commitment to this war on her life needed attention.

During the following week, after Sara's newest CT scan, Dyane watched her parents admit Sara to the hospital for a seven-day chemo treatment. Every drip of medication drove her immune system lower. Not only did Sara take a hard punch from her medication this time, immediately after Sara arrived back home, Dyane and Elizabeth also felt a blow of panic as Dr. White re-admitted Sara into the hospital with another fever. Nine days seemed to inch along for everyone while Sara stared at the same four walls of her white hospital room. One by one, the IVs cocktail splashed in an eerie rhythm within her vile. On this day, Dyane watched Sara's sleep become a most comforting friend.

***

Then, without warning, just six days following her discharge from a private room, an urgent phone call came into the Gillespie home.

"We have a liver—," the voice said.

Dyane rushed over to her mom's with little Cullen in tow. As he sat up in his highchair, everyone shuffled around. Their bodies pumped adrenaline like rushing rivers throughout their veins. With a phone in her mother's hand, she watched Sara's newest update begin its spread beyond her understanding.

At 4 a.m. on September the 3rd, when Sara's family assembled in an open waiting room. They sent Sara down to surgery with their prayers, Putter Paws, and an angel pinned to her shoulder. Before she left her side, Dyane stared at that gold pin. In a silent conversation with herself, she wrestled

mentally over the pin, which seemed to appear out of no-
where.

It's okay; she doesn't need an angel pin to remind her that God's angels are watching over her. That pin is just a reminder of God's presence and won't get any credit from me if this surgery goes well. She just needs to treasure it as a loving gift from one of her favorite nurses.

Moments later, Dyane watched Susan glare at the phone clamoring beside them. After a long sigh, she placed it up to her ear and looked off into the adjoining waiting room. She more than resisted communication with her ex-husband in Arizona, and Dyane cringed.

"No, Gerald, there's no need to come into Chicago. She's just going to be sleeping after the surgery. Yes, we'll call you when we find out," she said.

"Yes, yes, okay. *Okay, bye,*" she said.

Susan pushed the phone's off button with a strong thumb and rolled her eyes in exhaustion. With an intensified gaze, she looked Dyane straight in the eye.

"When she gets out of surgery, would you please call

your dad?" She asked.

Dyane gritted her teeth and nodded her head to support her mom's request. Because of the emergency surgery, she knew her mother's communication options had shrunk. In these moments, though, she disliked her oldest daughter's role. She empathized with her father's travel limitations from Arizona because of the last-minute notice but still disliked having to call him. Other non-attending family members struggled as well, and every person pled for an update. It all began to weigh heavy.

The waiting room felt bright, cold, and quiet while a meaningless television screen buzzed. The family ignored it as an option to pass time during Sara's transplant surgery. They found their only comfort in speaking to each other, drawing close, and grabbing a hand nearby to pray another prayer for Sara. Someone's head bobbed, reminding Dyane of the slow passing moments that turned into hours. Her heart felt heavy, almost crushing in the silence. She felt so small, so simple-minded. She held little to no understanding about this body she lived in day in and day out. Humbled, she considered the reality of her Creator, fearfully and wonderfully knitting her together in her mother's womb. In those still moments, she fixated on Cullen snuggled within his daddy's arms. She believed her son such a perfect blend of she and Joseph. Cullen amazed her and served as an excellent reminder of miracles. On the surgical table, Dyane imagined Sara receiving her own, held in the strong, loving, and masterful hands of the Great Physician himself.

Patience began to lag; some stood every half hour, stretched, and yawned. Some paced, and some tipped their heads back against the wall to catch more sleep. Dyane knew over the last few years her family lived this waiting story day in and out. Some days passed, numbing, slow, and familiar. During moments like these, though, they depended upon prayer support. Most of them, during the surgery, sat, knelt, fasted, and prayed without ceasing for her healing. Dyane rested her hand on her fist, imagining how helpless it must feel to someone who didn't know what to do at times like these.

The seconds ticked by in the waiting room, and everyone hoped a key prayer lifted on Sara's behalf somewhere in the world, making all the difference. Dyane's version of the perfect reply from God found Sara healed from this transplant. She imagined it; their lives flowing back to a normal routine, without moment by moment urgency. Sara then raised up to become the woman God recreated. Laying cancer to rest sounded awesome to her. A wife, mother, or professional interpreter for the deaf, all still remained options for Sara. Dyane hoped for her sister a lifetime of blessing and then to fall asleep one night much older and wiser, gazing upon Jesus. A great plan—simple but satisfying, unfolded in her mind. Yet, Dyane acknowledged that this self-willed package consisted of bubble-wrapped ideas, tied with her own self-satisfied bow. It left no room for God's will, His plan, or His glory.

At the word Sara left surgery, they all glanced around the room at each other. It concluded too soon. Susan, Jim, Dyane, and Elizabeth rose and left for the ICU, where the blackness which encompassed Sara's medicated sleep lifted from a foggy grey and brightened as the lights gradually reflected within her eyes. After their rush into the recovery room, Dyane watched Sara's hand lift towards her neck, where she felt nothing and awakened only for a moment. She felt her own stomach knot as her little sister's eyes fluttered. Susan took notice of Sara's missing tubes also, while her daughter's face twisted. Leaning against the wall during those elongating moments, with heads hung in silence. Susan gently glided her fingers over Sara's pale complexion to calm her. Afterward, they all returned to those in the family waiting room, appearing solemn and numb.

"When Sara woke from the anesthesia, we were told, if

she had no tubes in her neck, we would know that she didn't have the transplant," she said.

Her voice dropped then to an octave lower, as did her chin.

"I'm concerned more about her emotionally. We are *not* going to tell her until the doctors are with us," she stated.

***

On September 4th, the transplant doctor discharged Sara from the ICU and transported her to a patient room. Just before Dyane entered the pediatric room behind Sara's rolling hospital bed, a dim and yet familiar moment triggered her memory. Sara stayed in this room before. Settled in and still lying flat upon her bed, Sara rested under white sheets and pilled blankets. A few more entered the room in silence. Little conversation happened; Dyane didn't feel like speaking due to the tightening within her throat.

Their mom leaned over Sara, stroked her forehead with the palm of her hand, and then gave Sara's faded tan a kiss. Her words poured from her lips soft and low—

"Hi, honey," she said.

Sara became more aware and often blinked, trying to focus without her glasses. Dyane knew their mom's unmistakable touch compensated for Sara's missing hearing aids well. After becoming more alert, she looked around her room toward each of them. Then, with glazed eyes, she searched about her bed and twisted her head towards the IV pump.

"I'm not hooked up everywhere," she stated.

Susan inched closer and sat upon Sara's bed;

"Honey, they found lesions tucked *inside* of your liver."

Her voice broke, weakened by her tears. They dropped like rain from the corners of Susan's eyes and cascaded over her lips.

"The liver transplant wasn't successful; there's nothing that they can do…"

"I know—" Sara stated.

Dyane sniffed while wiping her eyes and drenching the tissue Joseph passed to her; he drew her close to his side. He kissed the top of her head and leaned her closer to his chest. Tears poured over everyone's cheeks. Sara's tears fell backward down her temples, over her ears, through her hair, and soaked into her pillow. Her mom also took turns wiping at her own eyes, wiping Sara's, blowing her own nose, and then leaned upon her husband in a state of exhaustion. Their hope of healing faded before their eyes.

***

Dyane readjusted on the green vinyl recliner, which sat next to Sara's bed. Due to Sara's need for a long nap after her surgery that afternoon, everyone but Dyane went home. The room sat darkened by the heavy light-blocking curtains, and Dyane welcomed her own sleep as the last few dramatic days exhausted all of them. Not long after a dream began, the phone's shrilling ring made Dyane jump from a reclining position. She stretched her hand for the phone, slipped on the seat, and fumbled around in tangled blankets before her fingers reached the receiver.

"Hello?" She said.

Her words hushed as if to make up for Sara's possible startle. Squinting in the darkness, Dyane didn't see her stir at all or recognize the woman's voice on the other end of the line. Dyane, however, picked up on an accent in her grogginess.

"Hello, is Sara Schreck there?"

"Oh no—she's sleeping. May I ask who's calling?" Dyane asked.

The woman's disappointment filtered through her gentle reply.

"This is Kathy Troccoli—" she said.

At that moment, Dyane sat up straighter, and her alertness restored. Her mind spun. *Is this the same Kathy Troccoli that I sing "Go Light Your World" with on the radio?*

"I was given Sara's name by a young man named Todd at one of my concerts a few weeks ago. He told me that she has cancer," she said.

In the dark, Dyane nodded.

"Yes, she actually just had an attempted liver transplant surgery yesterday. It wasn't successful. Would you like to call her again in a day or so when she's more awake?" Dyane asked.

Dyane's heart fluttered while she and Kathy both arranged a new time for her to call Sara back. Kathy came across eager to speak with Sara, and Dyane didn't know how she felt; she simply sat stunned in the silence after placing the receiver on the cradle. In the moments that followed, more thoughts and questions popped into her mind before she fell back to sleep. *How long ago was this concert that Kathy met Todd? She knew Kathy said she'd been given this room number weeks ago. Was she dreaming? Here she slept, awoken by Sara's hospital room phone with a call from Kathy Troccoli? God, only you made this moment possible. You returned Sara to this room for me to take this call at just the right time. Father, please let her discharge wait until after Kathy calls back...* As Dyane tucked and refolded her pillow underneath her head, she shivered, and goosebumps raced up behind her neck. Dyane just experienced a miracle.

***

When the next day arrived for Kathy to call back, their family felt a surge of joy and anticipation. With their phone appointment set, only one question remained in Dyane's mind after she returned from lunch and strolled into Sara's room.

"Did she call?" Dyane asked.

"Yes!" Sara exclaimed.

Her eyes sparkled, and her words climbed to a high pitch

at every remembrance of their relaxing conversation. The highlight for Sara—Kathy wanted to send her a few special things in the mail. This encouragement from Kathy Troccoli arrived at the perfect time and boosted their spirits. After only two days of recovery from her unsuccessful transplant surgery, Sara headed home.

***

Sara's lifted mood carried her into the week that followed. Dyane noticed by the end, however, it began to fade. Something changed Sara's tone during their recent phone conversations. Her somber feelings, took a lot of prodding to draw out.

"You are just so far away now," she said.

Sara's voice trembled. She considered what she heard— Sara, alone at home with their parents. Since Dyane and Joseph's job relocation almost thirty minutes away last spring, Elizabeth's and Neil's wedding, Cullen's birth, and the unsuccessful transplant surgery—her sister's emotional shift troubled her. During this journey, Sara depended upon either Elizabeth or Dyane to help her and sometimes, both of them together. She needed their presence. It felt now as if Sara reached through the phone crying out. Dyane squirmed where she stood and fidgeted with a pacifier. Did they abandon their sister? The weight upon Dyane's shoulders caused them to slump by a burden too heavy for her to carry.

Neither Elizabeth nor Dyane filled Sara's daily thirst for encouragement any longer. That reality broke Dyane's heart in ways no other conversation before. Dyane never intended to become a substitution for Sara's deeper relationship with God. Warmth traveled up her face. Her silent prayers became urgent while her thumb rubbed her temple, and the other gripped the phone receiver. She never wanted Sara to depend upon her in this way. Feeling alarmed, Dyane sought clarity. Prompted by her personal repentance and faith in God's plan, she surrendered Sara's felt needs through prayer. Difficult but necessary, Dyane accepted her own lack as eldest sister. Her lips tingled. At the wounding of her pride, Dyane questioned her motives before she spoke up and encouraged Sara again.

"I'll come soon…"

Chapter 12

Loving Through It

Grandma Irene filled her overnight shift at the hospital once again with eagerness. *Grandma* to all who knew her also became a grandma to Sara's nurses. On September 19th, Sara underwent chemotherapy again. She felt radiating warmth and comfort from her grandmother's presence. She rocked next to Sara's bed, crocheting another baby blanket for whoever blessed her with a great-grandchild next. Aware her dad planned to fly in from Arizona to see her, she knew her grandma fretted, and her nerves heightened to the possibility of his stopping at the hospital for a visit. Irene checked the doorway often—like a faithful watchdog on high alert.

His sudden entrance caused both Sara and her grandma to leap in surprise where they sat, and her stomach rushed towards her feet. When he arrived, he floundered in with the most unusual appearance. Wrinkles at the top of his dress slacks seemed pressed in, and his blonde hair rose a little in areas where he rested his head during the flight. He came in emotionally charged and ramped up to Sara's bedside. At that, he dropped upon her upper body, sobbing uncontrollably. Alcohol permeated the air and drifted into Sara's nostrils. She sat in shock, tensed, and pressed against the bed. Her adrenaline quickened while she attempted to catch a breath and return his weighty embrace. In a panic, she fumbled to keep her IV lines from being pulled out of place. Irene moved into action and dropped her crochet needle and blanket into her bag. Uncharacteristically bold and protective, she slid to the edge of the recliner and scolded him with a wagging of her finger.

"Gerald! Stop! *You cannot do that to her.* She needs positive, not negative right now!" she commanded.

During those long moments, nothing seemed to comfort him. Grief shook his body. Sara knew time passed like a freight train and he arrived unready to face her. She teared up as she tapped his back and felt the air escape her lungs the longer he crushed her. Sara also knew he also failed to accept the reality she faced until this moment. So many chemotherapy treatments kept them apart, the surgeries, the attempted liver transplant, the infections, and it all came and went without his presence, his permission, and his protection. Sara didn't know what to say. She loved him, felt sorry for him, and continued to pat his back until his sobbing subsided and he sat upright. She assured him, consoled him, and prayed for him as he retreated into the hallway that evening. She waved, holding onto the hope for another day, another God-given moment, to share the father and daughter conversation they needed to.

***

"Your counts are starting to get lower," Susan stated.

Sara shook her head and processed this news after her arrival home from the hospital.

"They are taking longer to come back up," she said.

As her mom stood, waiting for her to say something, Sara rested her elbow on the tile countertop. She then closed her eyes, ran a hand over her pale bald head and squeezed the back of her neck. This weight of discouragement, along with her father's grief, jarred Sara blow by blow. Even after nine chemotherapy treatments, her mother's news required time to process. Sara slipped off her stool as if in slow motion, wobbled up the stairs, and steadied herself by holding onto the railing. After finding the light switch, she entered her room and clicked the door closed. Sara took a seat upon her bed with the pen and card she brought up from the kitchen. With tear-filled eyes and a lump in her throat, she wrote a note, licked the envelope, and sealed it. Just before bed, Sara placed the envelope upon the downstairs counter, with hopes someone opened it before she came down in the morning.

Sara saw Susan's shadow pass in front of the nightlight and descend the stairs early the next day. As Susan filled her cup with clanking ice, Sara rose to the aroma of toasting bread. From the top of the stairs, she watched her mother's eyes skim the notes left by her husband in the wee hours of the morning and then notice her small envelope. She wrote the word *Mom* in large cursive letters on the front. Grinning, she split the paper with her fingernail and opened the card with a Bird of Paradise photo on the front. Sara's mom stood there for much longer than she expected, as if she read the single sentence over and over again.

"Mom, thanks for loving me! Love, Sara," it said.

Sara closed the bathroom door, glad her mom had found it. After she came out, however, her mom had disappeared. Sara stood at her mom's locked bedroom door and listened. Even with her hearing aids in, she heard only silence.

Loving Through It

***

Sara sat in Dyane and Joseph's miniature living room, watching Cullen play on the floor, toddling around with his barking doggie walker. Sara loved cheering on his shaky steps. He tipped over often, and his Auntie Sara cheered his effort so he'd rise again.

"Cullen, Auntie loves you," she said.

Sara felt a bit fatigued and laid on the brown carpeted floor next to his blocks. Kirby, Dyane's dachshund, nuzzled her nose into Sara's neck, causing her to giggle and squeal. The thirty minutes of hazy highways and side streets they drove to bring her to Dyane's house, made her eyelids feel heavy. The anticipation of their sleepover while Joseph traveled for work set Sara at ease all week. She felt so grateful to play with Cullen and stay overnight with her big sister. Like old times, they ate macaroni and cheese and visited around his routine.

After tucking Cullen into bed, Dyane emerged from his nursery with blankets for Sara's sleepover. Smiling, Sara sat up tall on the couch with a recent gift from Joseph's mom, Kathleen, in hand.

"Come and sit down, Dyane," she stated.

Dyane paused in her tracks and stared at her squirting lotion into her hand. Dyane rested a hand upon her stomach after setting the blankets down. With eyebrows raised, Dyane's voice strained.

"What are you doing?" Dyane asked.

"C'mon, sit down; it's been a long day. I want to share my new present with you," Sara stated.

Dyane appeared to feel uneasy as she tried to resist, but Sara refused to listen. So, she lowered on her own couch, where Sara guided Dyane's feet upon the pillows. Sara adjusted them from underneath.

"Um, Sara, this scenario needs reversing," Dyane stated.

Sara's eyes lifted and sparkled as she spread the thick cream upon Dyane's foot and ankle. Dyane returned her smile and fought laughter as her boney fingers seemed to tickle. Dyane wiggled her foot and cringed. So many thoughts wrestled within Sara's mind while her lighthearted voice filled the room. Dyane sighed deep and shook her head—Sara's heart ached. She longed to serve her sister a little and bless her as she has received blessings.

Soon after, Dyane collected the wrinkled sheets out of her over-stuffed linen closet and spread them over her couch. She tucked in every loose end, and Sara watched her pile on every extra blanket she owned to create a bed. Sara eagerly climbed in, snuggled between the covers but fought sleep because she loved the moments they spent talking. Rubbing her nose with her finger, she delved into the deep conversation she missed since Dyane left. Sara surprised Dyane with many thoughts about heaven and lingering questions, which filled up the rest of their evening together. Dyane knelt beside the couch, where Sara rested her head on a pillow. She loved the closeness.

"I feel like if I stay here, I win. But, if I go to heaven—I win, too," Sara said.

She lifted her sights toward Dyane's stenciled wall as if she wondered which prayer to pray. Then, Sara's eyes searched Dyane's, wondering why her sister hesitated to speak. Had she said something wrong? Sara felt her spirit wrestle within her expanding chest. Images flashed through her mind. Temptation, conflict, and peace all pulled at her in both scenarios. Sara almost felt guilt for wanting one more than the other. She began to blink faster and scratch the top of her hand.

"I just don't want to be in pain..." she said.

Sara began to feel pressure in her chest and allowed Dyane to capture her restless hand within her own, lay another hand over the top and begin a prayer. With eyes closed and Dyane's head bowed low, thoughts once stuffed to the back of Sara's mind, now lifted to God's ears. Sara ended with an *amen* and shuddered inside from the warm relief she felt fill her body. Dyane, in turn, blinked slow, her green eyes grew glassy, and she shared something Sara never expected to hear.

"I don't have any words to comfort you or fix this little sister; I just know the one who does, and so do you," she said.

At that moment, before Dyane switched off the living room light, they embraced. Sara needed that reassurance. Dyane kissed her bald head, leaving her all tingly as she offered a heartfelt goodnight.

***

As every chemo treatment took its lengthy course during those days—it seemed to shout at Sara—*this may be the last one.* She always wondered. But on the tenth treatment, Sara hit a delay due to low white blood counts. From November through December, Sara battled a fever, packed her bags for more hospital stays, adjusted to a new medication called Cisplatin, and made a couple of day trips to the clinic for blood and platelets. It all added to an already busy Christmas season. Around all of her hospital commitments, though, Sara began to make the best of her time with friends and family. She distracted herself by looking forward to fun moments while the battleground within Sara's mind and body continued. To collect her thoughts, she found it most relieving to write details down on paper. One day, Sara searched and found a yellow legal pad in the kitchen, and it appeared large enough to jot down a log of all that had happened the week before. With pen in hand, she recorded everything floating around her thoughts…

"On December 21st, I was told that my CT scan (taken 12/14) was positive. The radiologist said that one lesion looked larger. Dr. White disagreed. He thinks the rest look smaller. Dr. White also informed me that the transplant team had canceled a meeting that was supposed to take place that day at 2:30 p.m. Dr. White said that he would instead meet with the team on December 22nd. He plans on making them decide whether or not they are going to give me a transplant. One doctor says *no,* three say *yes.* I am to call on December 22nd to find out their decision. If they decline, I will have to look elsewhere."

With a deep stretch of her neck from side to side, Sara finished organizing her large collection of notes. She felt proud of herself for taking the time to get every detail down, knowing that remembering felt more and more challenging. Everyone made decisions for her, but she believed in the great benefits of Rush Presbyterian using her treatment study at their teaching hospital. She knew many worked hard for her healing, especially Dr. White. Sara didn't feel alone anymore. So many other little ones and parents also struggled in the pediatric unit, where she spent so much of her time. Many still waited for answers. Everyone needed hope. Many laid in bed lonely and frightened. All of the families made great sacrifices, like hers. Sara began to feel more empathy for them as she walked the same lonely road in in similar shoes.

***

As month after wintery month passed, Sara's twelfth chemotherapy round fell upon February 20th. Knowing it was a special day, her father's forty-fifth birthday, she drew within herself before calling him. Sara didn't have a gift of encouragement to offer to soften the news. The birthday gift she wanted to give instead became a bitter dose of reality, a day which marked Sara's final chemotherapy treatment.

Chapter 13

Nothing To Lose

Sara meandered onto the wooden stage, ready for this day. She scanned the mass of students that sat in the Illiana Christian High School chapel service, all of whom stared back at her. Sara cleared her throat, smoothed out her notes, smiled, and spoke with renewed confidence.

"I have Adrenal Cortical Carcinoma. This disease has affected me physically, emotionally, and spiritually. I have now had twelve chemo treatments with a medication called Mitotane. I've experienced infections, sensory neuropathy—which is a numbing of my hands and feet, and hair and hearing loss. I have kidney problems and have also suffered from malnutrition. I have undergone many tests like ultrasounds, Cat Scans, MRIs, blood tests, spinal taps, and nerve conduction. During my first surgery, the doctors found an eight-inch tumor on my adrenal gland. They also found lesions upon my liver, which they described as looking like Swiss cheese. I now live with a twelve-inch scar on my abdomen. During my second surgery, the surgeons took a biopsy, and all of the visible lesions were removed. I went into shock after that surgery—Christian artist Kathy Troccoli called me, and Make-A-Wish paid for my family and me to go on a trip to Hawaii. We had so much fun and were finally able to relax for a while. Three weeks ago, I had another scan where the doctors saw lesions; even more have shown up in my attempted transplant surgeries. My faith in God is what keeps me going. I now live each day like I might die tomorrow. May each of you also live like you'll die tomorrow and die knowing you'll live forever…"

While exiting the stage, the Illiana students' applause became thunderous. With the guiding help of a teacher's arm, the stage steps led her slowly into an ocean of people. Even though tired, she welcomed hug after hug and gained a little more strength with every loving word. Some hugs and words of encouragement came from those she failed to know personally over the last two and a half years of treatment. Regardless, for her, each student became family on the day she shared her story.

***

Susan kept careful track of Sara's social calendar in her black hairdressing appointment book; it sat upon her countertop, remained open, and filled with notes. Susan penciled down everything with meticulous detail, and Sara flipped backward through the written log over the previous few months. Calling Dyane over to see it, she fanned the pages in a reverse motion and noticed some of the most filled weeks began last November and stretched into the present day.

"Sara to Chicago—visit Maribeth at Lana's house, 11/14—Chemo #10 (possible last), back into hospital—counts not good, 11/23—home from the hospital, 11/28—getting platelets and blood, 11/30—hospital for fever, 12/9—bowling alley—Sara, Alli, and Toby's celebration, 12/14—CT Scan, 12/21—Clinic, 12/21-Lissa and Leigh here for Chinese, 12/27—Sara, Elizabeth, Maribeth, Lana-Chicago trip, 1/3-Chemo #11, 1/9—home, 1/13—Clinic, 1/17—Sara getting blood platelets, 1/18—fever, 1/23—Sara-eye exam, 1/25—Sara-Black Hawks game, 2/3–Illiana Homecoming-Sara out with Leigh, 2/20–Dad's birthday & Sara's last chemo, 2/26—home, 3/5—hospital w/ fever, 3/10—home, 3/15—CT scan, 4/1—Deer Creek Church program and sleep-over."

Dyane stood there and shook her head at her sister and mom. Her eyes widened.

"Just reading all the dates and activities you've got here makes me feel exhausted!" Dyane said.

Sara agreed, in spite of the setbacks she faced so often, something propelled her forward with vision and purpose. She chose to press on, truly living like tomorrow might never come.

***

The morning sunlight poked through the blinds and cast a combination of lined shadows and sunlit beams into the room. Every pattern strung across Sara's floral comforter, her pillow, and her face as she slept in that morning. Sara squinted and swiped at her eyes—then stretched her arm across the piles of pillows beside her with a long graceful cascade of fingers. She then tilted her head and yawned while looking over at her silent alarm clock. She didn't set it anymore; she didn't see any point since her ears failed to hear the morning clamor. Her sleep, unusual and restless, played constant visions and role-plays all night. They taunted her mind and kept her from falling off to sleep with ease.

Sara prepared well for her flight from Chicago to Arizona to visit her dad that week. Just before she and her mom left for the airport, Sara made an announcement.

"This is my nothing-to-lose trip," she stated.

Susan nodded while her hands gripped the wheel, but Sara wondered if her mom heard or understood what she said. With each jar of the road, Sara's curiosity deepened and got the better of her. She asked Susan what she heard her say.

"You forgot your blue shoes for the trip?" Susan asked.

Sara snorted with laughter, and Susan followed suit. Sara thought she heard her mom say something about shoes and turned up her new hearing aides. They took some getting used to. Hearing things right the first time, like her mom, also took some practice. A few weeks ago, when she got fit for them, she admitted to feeling sorry for herself, but her mom had a way of making losing her hearing a little more fun than she anticipated.

"Mom, this is my *nothing-to-lose trip. Did you hear me?*" Sara restated and asked. This time, enunciating every word slow and clear.

"Oh! Um, I think so, but you'll need to explain this nothing to lose trip a little more," Susan stated.

Smiling, Sara felt victorious over their successful exchange and bounced a little on the passenger seat.

"Okay, Mom. Well, I've made decisions. I'm not going to be intimidated by Dad. I'm just going to show him the same love and grace I've received, even if he's struggling. I'm not going to fixate on the fancy places we go, the expensive things he gives me, or on the adventures he wants me to experience. Even if I feel nervous, I'm going to share Jesus with him as God leads me to. He may hate me for it or may turn around and give his life to Christ; I don't know. I have nothing to lose. Whatever happens, happens, but I won't ignore this burden on my mind anymore. I guess that's why I'm calling this my nothing to lose trip," Sara said.

She stared out the window at the oncoming traffic stopped in its tracks across the median.

Susan nodded.

"It makes sense, honey," Susan replied. "It's best not to assume anything and seize the moment while you have it. I know you've been praying for him, and I promise we will too."

Sara also remembered Dyane feeling a similar way when she visited their dad in Arizona. It didn't take long during Dyane's brief summer visits growing up before she realized her words fell on his deafened ears. Sara remembered her sister often cried tears of intense aggravation and disappointment when she'd return home. The urgency she felt every time she visited him, and his antagonism after a few drinks caused her immeasurable anxiety. Dyane realized his soul remained God's responsibility, though, not hers. Once she surrendered the weighty aim she carried every time she saw him, she felt more loving compassion for him as her dad. She also felt released from her self-appointed duty to save him from the trappings of sad memories, regrets, addiction, anger, and his ultimate rejection of her faith in God. She also remembered Dyane forgiving their dad for everything she blamed him for, extending more grace to him because Jesus extended His grace to her. Sara's heart leaped when she heard her sister say she felt freed to love him. Sara then, in turn, dropped all of her own selfish expectations and prayed over this trip. The sisters agreed Jesus wanted to save their dad and give him a new life. However, their forgiveness and surrender to His will allowed them to become liberated and free first. Sara turned toward her mom's voice after Susan tapped her on the arm to get her attention.

"Hey, make sure you stay out of the sun," Susan stated.

Sara grimaced and teased her a little.

"Uh yea, Mom, even after three years of chemo, it still poses a problem in Arizona. I know Dr. White doesn't want me to, but I'm still planning to get into Dad's pool. I've got my sunblock and hat; I'll be fine," Sara said.

Susan's eyebrows raised, and she faked a nervous grin.

Sara exhaled the anxiety away and turned back to her observance of traffic until she arrived at Midway Airport. She knew she played it safe up until now. Trying to avoid exposure on a regular basis, Sara faithfully sat under an umbrella and watched her family swim in the pool at home. If she ever felt adventurous, her wide-brimmed sunhat and layers of sunblock prepared her for a thrilling float inside a blowup paddle boat. She recalled it taking a lot of effort to get in and out of it, exhausting her. Shadowed underneath the barriers to the sun, Sara pretended to have fun with everyone while she drifted upon the water. On this trip, she instead longed for the joy and excitement of placing her hearing aids upon the patio table. Then, dipping her full thin body underneath the cool water's surface. Sara planned to let it rise over every pore, then envelope and submerge her before rising up to a float.

Arizona welcomed her again, now a young mature woman of sound mind. As she exited the plane, Sara forced herself to stand tall. Faith clothed her countenance, fed her hope, and offered her strength to face her father. In the spirit of love, boldness, courage, and trust, it drove her forward. No matter the risk—she knew she had nothing to lose. The sauna-like heat wrapped her. It felt good after the chill of the plane.

"Sara!" Gerald exclaimed.

His toothy white smile drew her, and he wrapped her tight in his muscular bear hug.

***

Sara's trip, while lacking everything she hoped, avoided becoming a total flop. She felt satisfied, knowing she planted seeds and said what she needed to her dad. Now home, she readied herself for her Illiana Junior, Senior banquet. She didn't bring home a tan, but her joy over the event made her glow. Sara primped all afternoon and finally entered the kitchen for her mom's final touches. Sara, beyond giddy—posed in full make-up, clothed in a white bathrobe and shimmering bald head. Dyane reached for her side, laughing while she reached for her camera.

"Wait—do *that* again, Sara!" Dyane squealed.

Sara's hands shifted her robe in all different contortions for the camera as if posing for her paparazzi. Sara's smile burst larger with every click. It took everything within her not to wiggle on the barstool while her fingernails gained a new coating of pink polish. Sara rested her glasses upon the tip of her nose as she inspected her mother's artistry.

Dyane's cheek pressed into the backside of her camera. At her call, Sara perked up with a little hop and struck another smiling pose solely for the women in her mother's kitchen that day. The camera captured Sara at just the right moment. Dyane snorted and placed her index finger underneath her nose. Rather than get dressed, Sara continued to model and giggle in her terrycloth bathrobe. Sara lifted her folded collar, tilted her chin downward, and then lifted her eyes up towards Dyane's lens with a playful glance. Sara stood before them swinging as if draped in the most spectacular dress. She appeared to adore its fluffy comfort and warmth until the very last moment.

Not long after, the family cocker spaniel yapped at the sound of the doorbell. Shaking her hands at the top of the stairs, Sara checked her makeup in the bathroom mirror and popped her lips together. Finally dressed for her evening, Dyane observed her sister's cascade down the steps in a much more mature gliding fashion. Sara's cream satin gown embraced her silhouette in timeless elegance. Around her neck, a satin band held a haltering design of fabric, which flattered Sara's slender body and covered her raised port area. Dyane felt everyone's eyes lock on her sister as she approached the doorway. Shooing the dog away, Sara welcomed Philip, one of her dearest friends. When Dyane captured his handsome appearance from the dining room, she grinned, enjoying Sara's sweet smile and greeting. Philip complimented her, and Dyane watched her sister attempt to cover her blushed cheeks. After meandering around the leaping dog, Sara's voice began to quiver with a laugh before she covered her mouth with polished fingertips. She positioned herself in front of the family room fireplace, where Dyane continued snapping the pictures. Upon first glance at the clear box in Philip's hand, Dyane knew the red rose corsage, and its silver ribbon complemented her sister's dress. Sara shook a little as she opened it after Philip handed her. Susan helped pin the boutonniere upon the flap of his suit before assisting Sara. Dyane stood close enough to them both to enjoy the melding of her light perfume and his cologne. Concluding the exchange, Sara covered her cheeks with both hands again. Behind the lens, Dyane's eyes glimmered with tears, and their mom wiped at the corners of her eyes also.

Till That Day Comes

Dyane considered where Sara now stood a little more than two weeks ago while healing from her fourth surgery. Dyane filled her lungs with all the joy in the room. She observed her sister steal a glance up at Philip and marveled that this special day arrived. Sara held onto hope for this moment. Through the whole surgical process, she anticipated being his date at their senior banquet. Philip smiled down at her, and Sara placed a free hand upon her stomach. Dyane felt her own insides melt as he looked upon her. They exchanged a grin, and Sara's lashes fluttered before the tall, dark, and handsome young man before her. Dyane noted his character and the light within his eyes welcoming one of his dearest friends to join him on an unforgettable evening. Dyane sighed, feeling grateful for his loving kindness. It drew her little sister into a storybook event, giving Sara memories she dreamt about for so long.

As they all stepped into the trimmed backyard and onto the deck, their mom got to work. She adjusted Sara's dress, her little shoulder capped jacket, Sara's cream satin beret, Phil's flower, and both of their hands into a photogenic position. Orange flowering vines draped across the overhead pergola like miniature chandeliers. The ferns peeked out from behind the wooden benches, and pinky-peach azaleas softened the beautified the scene. After handing her jittery mother the camera, Susan took quick steps backward. She snapped away, capturing moments unseen in typical senior banquet pictures. As the flashes lit up the early evening, a few chatted on the benches nearby, and Dyane glued her sight upon Sara's countenance. She stood tall, shoulders back, and chin tilted toward Philip. Sara's eyes also spoke a message meant for anyone listening, and to Dyane, it declared, *this is my moment.*

Dyane smiled, wiped at her lashes again with the back of her finger, and cleared her throat softly. Dyane fought the expansion of her throat where the pressure built. A few tears threatened to spill, but she only allowed her heart to cry out with joy. *Thank you, God! Thank you, God, for giving Sara this gift on her eighteenth birthday! She looks like a woman standing before me—so confident, so proud to be on Philip's arm, so at peace with who she has become...*

***

In the days following, Sara looked forward to her high school graduation ceremony. Regardless of Sara's inability to become an official graduate of her senior class, she zipped up her white gown and waited amongst friends. Before anyone sat in the crowd, the ladies of her family made efforts to stick the graduation cap onto Sara's bristling head with double-sided adhesive tape. Soon after, Lissa, one of Sara's closest friends, walked up to the front stage and settled behind the podium. She began her speech by describing Sara's three-year battle with cancer, her inspiring faith, and her testimony. After Lissa's introduction to the full auditorium and presentation of the engraved plaque on behalf of the entire Illiana Christian High School graduating class, Sara caught hold of her friend and embraced her tight. Dyane noticed her sister wiping her reddening face from where she sat. She then began to fan herself with the program on her sister's behalf. Dyane also took note of Sara's shimmer of tears as she stepped behind the podium. Applause erupted and encouraged her until Sara took another deep, shaky breath in the mic and regained her composure. With each word she spoke, her sentences progressed with an urgency and clarity untypical of a young woman of only eighteen.

"I want to thank you, Illiana, as a whole, for making this happen. The Lord has really blessed me with awesome classmates to graduate with. I am so thankful for everyone making me feel welcome whenever I came to visit. It was so neat to go there and experience the different individual personalities that each person had. I was able to get uplifted in all areas of my life from each one of you. I hope I uplifted some of you too.

What are we waiting for? Let's turn this world upside down for Christ! In the name of Jesus—*let's do it!*

I love saying, 'Live like you'll die tomorrow…die knowing you'll live forever.' Live one day at a time because the Lord doesn't promise us a tomorrow.

Even though I don't have a real diploma in my hands, I will always consider and be proud to call Illiana Christian, my high school that I graduated from.

Thank you, and I will love you always."

Sara's thanks and personal challenge to the crowd moved them all to tears again. Even with blurred eyesight, they all stood to give her a standing ovation. Illiana's love, respect, and gratefulness for Sara Schreck solidified that very moment.

After the presentation of the diplomas, Sara's classmate, Kevin, closed the ceremony by asking every graduate to do something unique that evening.

"Hold on to each memory and do your class the honor of remembering them...it's good to be alive; it's good to be young. We're high school graduates, but our education is far from over. So we live on, as the Bible says, humbly with our God and as strangers here in reverent fear."

***

Weeks later, after returning from a summer camping trip to Michigan with her family and friends, Sara's Aunt Marie sat upon a kitchen stool and gushed over her family's camping trip with Sara.

"Sara tried everything we did... she wanted to go hiking with everyone, so we found some big walking sticks and began our hike. When Sara got tired, we stopped, and when she struggled to continue, William carried her piggyback. Even when tired, Sara took in our surroundings and said how beautiful everything was. She would say how she would hike in heaven and not get tired. Sara wanted to go to the beach with us, so we made a makeshift tent to block the sun because she said if she was in the sun, she might get cancer! She was always saying things like that...

When we would go out to eat, and someone was sitting by us smoking, Sara would love to take off her hat to reveal her bald head, and people would put out their cigarettes right way—Sara was even a natural bug repellent!" Aunt Marie stated.

Sara laughed out loud and covered her face with a widened hand. No one in the room held back their amusement, and after their tearful giggles subsided, Dyane sighed at the mental images her aunt conveyed. Whatever worry she felt about her sister's recent trip, passed and her shoulders dropped in relief. Before Sara's vacation, Dyane struggled to envision Sara keeping up the pace, but now, she realized everyone committed to assisting her. She felt grateful no one left her behind, and everyone helped her fulfill her goals for her camping adventure. She beamed, thankful also for Sara, who offered true comic relief for everyone the night of their return.

***

Late into the summer, the sticky air prompted Dyane to gather Cullen and buckle him into his car seat. With his diaper bag and a full sippy cup, they drove for thirty minutes in late morning expressway traffic. Along the way, Cullen sang most of the way to his grandma's house for another swim day.

"Dyane, please help me. Sara needs help getting into the water," Susan stated.

Sara's inflatable boat waited for her while it hovered and rocked upon the surface. Dyane received her son from Susan, dipped Cullen into the pool, blew air bubbles, and set him onto Sara's floating ship. While she held him in front, both Dyane and her mom took turns pulling both Sara and Cullen around the pool, swirling them round and round. As Cullen began to fuss and claw at the white plastic, it became clear he wanted to maneuver out of the boat toward Dyane to nurse. Sara's face appeared pale. Her expelled energy to kept him from going overboard, so Dyane guided the rocking boat toward the ladder and swept her dripping son up to the deck. Susan floated near the boat near the ladder and supported Sara, guiding her daughter's legs over the side and pulled them towards the ladder. The current pressed against the boat as Sara and their mom lifted and led her body up the steps from behind. Sara's pale legs trembled with goosebumps. Weak, she welcomed the towel Dyane handed her to set upon her boney shoulders. Her teeth chattered while the wind blew upon the droplets of water and the sun's heat warmed her skin.

After dressing inside, Dyane grabbed a cup from the

cabinet and caught a glance at Susan's open August activity calendar. It began with an 8/5-Cookout, 8/9-Clinic, and Carson's Fashion Show-Sara Model's for it!' Dyane's eyes widened at the news as memories of her own fashion shows came to mind. She wondered why Sara kept tight-lipped; the opportunity impressed Dyane. Dyane pictured her in a gown, making her turn on a narrow runway and fulfilling another common dream they shared as teens.

As time went on, even though Sara's excitement seemed to build over the event, Dyane took even more interest in her initial silence about it. A few years ago, she heard the endless chatter about Sara's desire to model in a local fashion show, but in this season of Sara's life, it seemed no different than any another high-profile activity she refrained from discussing.

Chapter 14

Why Me?

On the brightest of sunny mornings, Dyane awoke achy and sore after not sleeping in her own bed. Staying overnight, her mom and Jimmy's home always left her feeling stiff. She entered Sara's room and began rummaging through one of the closets, searching for a sweatshirt. As she slipped an oversized one over her head, she felt wrapped in warmth again. After opening the window shades, Dyane watched the sun pour its rays upon the brown carpeting, then observed Sara's slow rise out of bed. Hunching over, Sara set glasses upon her face and plugged a hearing aid into each ear. Dyane drew close to her side, looking for something to do to help her sister. As she stood waiting, Sara stared into her eyes and confided with Dyane in a low whisper.

"Dyane, I was up late last night praying…and crying."

With a sheepish look of embarrassment, she confessed to asking God a question in the middle of the night.

"I asked Him, 'Why is this happening to me?' and now I

regret it."

Dyane swallowed hard. She stood near the nightstand, stunned, and stared at her sister. Sara shifted her eyes away. When she returned Dyane's gaze, skin creased between her eyebrows. Dyane wondered for a split second if Sara expected a lightning bolt to strike her.

"I know deep down; it's not really my place to ask that," Sara stated.

"Like, I know God loves me. He's not left me through any of this. I've watched Him answer so many prayers; it's crazy. He healed me from that dangerous legion on my cheek. He allowed Lissa and I to become friends again. You're not far away anymore, and Cullen's here. Elizabeth found Neil. I got to go to Hawaii for my Make-A-Wish trip. I'm graduated from Illiana now. Kathy Troccoli called me. Dad's heart is opening a bit. Plus, I'm not the same person I once was. I know I've grown, and I've grown closer to God, but I honestly couldn't help it. I've held out for so long, resisting the temptation, fighting the urge within me to ask—I just couldn't wait any longer," she said.

Sara looked down at her naked feet, and Dyane hugged her while letting out the deep sigh she suppressed. Dyane empathized with her distress. She remembered three years of cancer, the surgeries, the treatments, infections, losses, her pain, and the twelve weeks of long in-patient chemotherapies. She almost felt relieved Sara's courage kicked in to overcome her fear and ask God the long-avoided question.

After only a few minutes of conversation up in Sara's bedroom, Dyane heard the phone ring in the downstairs kitchen. Then, she heard their mom calling up the stairwell—

"Sara, it's for you," she said.

Dyane watched from the upper hall with curiosity as Sara received the phone's handset. After putting it up to her ear, Sara nodded and nodded again.

"Yes, okay, thank you," she said.

Their mom, Susan, received the phone from Sara's outstretched hand. Climbing the stairs, she giggled while carefully holding the railing; Sara entered the bedroom again with her mom close behind. She shook her head, breathless with laughter. As she did, she made a decisive proclamation.

"I'm never asking why again," she stated.

Susan turned up her own hearing aids and sat on the bedside while Dyane finished pulling up Sara's comforter. Then, she fumbled over her words and leaned against the dresser.

"What happened? Who was it?"

"Well, it was someone from *The Back To God Hour* television show, and they asked me for an interview!"

Goosebumps trickled up and down Dyane's body, and her wide eyes reflected glassy tears. Stunned, she pulled the throw pillow she grasped closer to her chest. Their eyebrows lifted, and they stared at each other, grinning. In shock, Dyane's quick blinking reflected her awe over the timing of the call. She knew in her gut God wanted them to know something. Uncertain, Dyane wondered if He *wanted* to answer Sara's question. They discussed it, further reminded of His clear awareness. Assured, they realized God still held a divine purpose for Sara's life with cancer. Dyane and Sara gripped hands and squealed. Even though she fought the normal questions like—*Why me?* They both knew and agreed that Sara held a unique God-given opportunity to encourage people. Dyane's mind raced as she attempted to grasp the potential impact of her testimony. Not only broadcast within the United States but abroad, Dyane reminded Sara about those facing death without hope all over the world. Sara's hands returned her squeeze, and she nodded her head as one not surprised at all.

Reflecting alone later in the day, Dyane nestled into a chair while Cullen napped and reconsidered the *Why me* question Sara asked God. Dyane hesitated to ask the question throughout her own life, thinking it too much or irreverent. After what she witnessed, she reconsidered the idea. It seemed like such a normal human question, one that she herself felt the temptation to ask during Sara's journey. However, as the well-timed phone call came in from *The Back To God Hour*, it melted her doubts away. In one moment, Sara's asking the question propelled her toward feelings of guilt, shame, and embarrassment. In the next moment, God revealed His all-knowing, special plan to Sara. Dyane believed God desired to encourage her sister, not harm her in the most terrifying fire of her life. Dyane knew of Sara's nervousness to receive any answer by the way she confessed on her bedside that morning, the way she said she cried out and sought God. Not taken back by Sara's question or even her frustration—He answered, knowing the question long before she asked it. God never kept her waiting for His reply, and today, Dyane saw their relationship with her own eyes. All of His grace-filled promises continued to pour out upon her sister, and the realization made her heart ache and her nose sting. He never failed to show up or answer an eighteen-year-old young woman with questions. She stared out the picture window, for she knew she also wanted to ask questions and prayed for His merciful grace in her own life as well.

***

On the next sun-filled day, Cullen splashed and threw his toys into the baby pool upon her parent's patio. While watching him, Dyane wondered just how many people already experienced Sara's fun personality, creativity, and passionate, bold witness for Christ. Just days away, she knew Sara looked forward to the Back to God interview. Dyane wrapped her waist with a beach towel and knelt by his side. She also allowed her mind to wander back to memories of her sister Sara in this backyard and her life before cancer. Everything changed. Though one thing stayed the same, Sara's drive for a thrilling adventure of her own reminded people often; their family needed constant prayer.

Dyane glanced down at her son Cullen in the swirling water. Now eighteen months old, her heart pounded deeply inside of her chest. She smiled down at him, even though fear messed with her mind. Just over twenty peddling motions upon his tricycle separated him from the nearby road-way, willing to suck him into traffic. She gritted her teeth at the thought and asked—*would God send someone to watch over Cullen like He did for Sara at this age?* At that, Dyane stroked her son's wet blonde hair and swiped the splashes of water droplets off of his face.

Afterward, Dyane breathed another sigh of relief. She tipped her face up towards the sun, and with her eyes closed, she let the heat soak into the surface of her skin. In light of Sara's turbulent past, she thought about Sara and how the years affected them both. No longer a stranger to scary or life-threatening moments or Sara's recent *Why me* question, Dyane considered questions of her own, *why wouldn't Sara have cancer? Why wouldn't I have cancer one day?* Considering those weighty thoughts, Dyane realized God's challenge to her own ideas about life, about suffering, His sovereignty, and greatest of all—His love for His people.

In this process, Philippians 4:13 suddenly came alive;

"I can do everything through him who gives me strength."

Chapter 15

Wedding Plans

Early in the summer of 1995, Sara asked her closest friends Alli, Lissa, Alice, and Leigh to do something that made Dyane both cringe and laugh. She asked the girls to write a letter to her, but not just any letter, a letter written as if she already entered heaven. Sara wanted to know what they would say to her, about her, and how they felt about Sara being gone. Dyane's dear sister even wanted her best friends to actually read the letter to her while she videotaped them. As both Dyane and their mother reviewed the video recordings, they witnessed Sara's joy throughout the whole process. Sara's friend Alli read her letter first in an upbeat tone and in deep reflection.

"Dear Sara,

How is home? Your goodbye still really hasn't hit me. I feel as though you left so much of yourself behind here. I have a little Sara to grasp on to. Do you even know what a spiritual warrior you were—you were always too humble to ever let yourself think so, though. I'm trying to keep my mind on the thought that it's now my turn to be a spiritual friend, my turn to guide someone through the thorns and spikes on their own sandy path. You, my dear one, turned my sand into concrete. Every now and then, it would crack, but cracks can be re-filled.

When I heard you left for home, I shed some tears, but merely because you entered the home, you have been longing for. No more pain, bloated bellies, disagreements, and sour stomachs. But a community of fellow lovers of Christ, purity, joy, and once again, I'm sure you're feeding everyone their share of your special pasta recipes.

Sara, I love you more than bunches, and I miss you more than anyone can imagine. But you showed me a hope that has now become a real vision—Jesus Christ. Your life was a constant growth. That's what I desire. My desire was once your desire. I want the hope that you now have. Your motto is my motto—live like you'll die tomorrow, die knowing you'll live forever.

Love, Alli"

As Alli finished, Alice searched Sara's eyes as she poured out her heart. Alice ignored the camera and spoke only to her—

"Dear Sara,

I want you to know how much your life still impacts mine. I now know your death was in God's plan and design; He used you in so many amazing ways. At the time, He used you to teach me courage to stand up and be bold for God, not to fear death, and not to ask, "Why Me?" Today, God is still using your death and life to teach me—and I say death because had you lived on earth—the impact on my life would not be the same. God is really showing me His sovereign control of our lives. It is amazing how at certain times, I think of you out of the blue because you are on my heart. I'll never forget the sleepovers and how it was sooo cold in the room, talking about infant baptism, you telling me in the hospital that you were glad your hair fell out with the chemo because you would have probably pulled it out. I will always remember how you would use your baldness to get to the front of the lines when we would go out, and oh, your incredible burps! I can still see you wearing your rugby shirt and doing my hair for a dance in

your mom's salon—even though you had none yourself. And, I still remember you and me at the hospital
and your determination to share your faith in God with
the nurses—while you were throwing up and shirtless!

Your death was not for nothing—God used you to
display His glory and the goodness of His plans. I'm
sure God will continue to use you in my life as well as
countless others, not for nothing, but for so much more
than you ever knew.

Love in Christ, Alice."

By the time October winds began to blow, Sara hadn't
finished the taping project. She knew her time grew short
and felt an urgency to complete the video recordings with
Lissa and Leigh, as they hadn't read their letters yet. Sara
set the day, and once it had arrived, Sara spoke to the lens
by introducing her friends. However, the introduction also
revealed her weakened and fragile body. Leigh read her letter and appeared nervous as her eyes searched for her friend
behind the camera.

"Sara,

I think back three years ago when we first met at the

Illiana homecoming dance. I came over by you because you were crying about a certain guy. Wow, someone's priorities sure changed since then, didn't they! Isn't God so awesome that He used a moment like that to start a friendship between us? One that changed my life!

Paul had a thorn in the flesh that God didn't remove. He said, "I have fought the good fight," in 2 Timothy 4:7, just as you did Sara. And even though God felt your work on earth was important for Him, He felt that it was more important for you to be with Him now.

Eighteen years is not very long, but I know that you have made an impact on more people's lives than most people could do in eighty years. I don't think I could ever thank you enough for the way you touched my life. I miss you so much already! I'm going to miss going out together, staying at the hospital, having our long talks, and I'll miss those great dinners you made me! But I'll especially miss praying together because that is one thing you really helped me with. I know we will all miss you at the bank; you brightened everyone's day by just being there! I know I will be with you in just a short while, and I know you will be waiting to greet me. So, until we meet again in heaven, I LOVE YOU

BUNCHES!

Your friend, Leigh."

Lissa went last. Her words, instead of being shaky, sounded as if inspired. Sara looked on thrilled, for her words came across as the tribute and encouragement she always hoped they would be. Because of that, Susan and Dyane both felt hot tears blur their eyes as they watched and listened to the last tearful, broken sentences Lissa spoke.

"Dear beautiful Sara,

'Do not let your hearts be troubled. You believe in God; believe also in me. My Father's house has many rooms; if that were not so, would I have told you that I am going there to prepare a place for you? And if I go and prepare a place for you, I will come back and take you to be with me that you also may be where I am' (John 14:1-3).

You have given your life and your whole self to Christ that He may use you to bring others to Him. Sara, it seems as though we have been friends forever. Friendship and love never end when it's in Christ. I won't say good-bye because I live today knowing that we will be together again in heaven. I have so many wonderful memories.

Remember the hot air balloon ride, the shopping sprees, the birthday parties, formal dresses, graduation, and the quiet times that we talked? I hold these memories in my heart and will never let them go.

I love you, Sara,

Lissa"

Lissa's voice broke as her tears welled within her eyes. The overwhelming emotion then closed her throat to a soft muffle. As she finished, Dyane watched Lissa take hold of Sara. Tears spilled down their faces.

Dyane felt like Sara's request for letters not only awe-inspiring but wise. Each one spoke so selfless, loving, stretching, soul searching, and heartfelt—reflecting an inexpressible thread of unity. The end resulted in an intimate moment that only they shared and that captured their eternal bond like nothing else. Dyane wondered about the days to come, the days of their remembering those moments together as true gifts of God's grace. She wondered about their preparation for the days like weddings, babies, and their own losses when missing Sara felt deeper and raw. Seasons of hospital overnights finding their end, the fade of drawn-out talks on

Sara's bed, and the grief process alone all ripped at Dyane's heart. She felt grateful, imagining their days and nights filled and focused on college activities and studies again. Considering the milestones before them, she shared their joy. She also empathized with their loneliness and longing for the best friend who once spurred them on to live as if each day as if their last. Impossible for anyone to take their place, she remembered when God chose them to walk by Sara's side as her closest companions. He chose them. God knew Sara needed them for the hardest trial of her life, and God knew they needed her. Regardless of the days to come, everyone learned how to choose gratefulness for just one more day, one more hour, and one more minute with Sara.

***

Both Dyane and Sara nestled down upon Sara's bed among a few stuffed animals and settled in by leaning up against a large backrest of pink and blue pillows. A yellow legal pad rested upon Dyane's lap, and her fingers twirled a pen. She sat ready to make a written list of special possessions Sara wanted to be passed on to family and friends soon. Adjusting the back pillows just right, Dyane's soft grin reflected the peace and joy she felt in her soul. She loved spending more time with her little sister and counted this moment as a privilege. A lump in her throat grew and proved difficult to get rid of by clearing it. Dyane swiped her eyes as Sara got up from the bed again and looked around her bedroom—she didn't seem to want to forget anything. Giveaways piled in front of her feet as Dyane recorded her sister's specific instructions line by line. Time passed quickly while reminiscing over old plaques, bedroom décor, and clothing she planned to give away. Lighthearted with laughter, Dyane found this easier than she originally anticipated. Her glimmering eyes followed Sara around the room, knowing Sara placed so much thought into each gift she intended to give away. Every piece of jewelry, her favorite perfume bottles, her marked Bibles, framed pictures, floppy hats, and a trove of gifts given to her while sick—all landed on the list with a new home. Every gift she received over the years of treatment held a story, and both sisters prepared to re-gift them with Sara's love and reasoning attached.

"The diamond horseshoe necklace, I want Lizzy to have, and I want you to have my ruby necklace…" Sara stated with a grin, and Dyane caught her breath, unable to look away from her.

"Thank you so much, Sara," said Dyane.

Sara's loosening grip on the treasures she held on Earth reminded Dyane of the impossibility of taking even one item with her. However, once they finished, Sara confessed to the one treasure on Earth paining her most, and almost impossible for her to surrender.

Sara searched the depths of Dyane's green eyes at length and paused. Dropping her gaze, Dyane watched her sister stare at her empty palms. Sara blew a lengthy exhale from her lips; her chin quivered, and then Sara's voice broke into a hyperventilating cry.

"I don't want to leave my baby," Sara stated.

She tried to hold her breath and then choked through another cascading flow of tears. Sara wiped her lips and nose with her sleeve, and Dyane reached for her. They embraced and leaned against each other for more than thirty minutes—sobbing over the heaviest and most withheld revelation upon Sara's heart Dyane knew of. Dyane searched her own soul, counting the cost of this true sacrifice. For she knew her son Cullen, Sara's only nephew, her pride and joy—might never comprehend the depth of Sara's love for him or how much she prayed over him. Dyane now understood more than ever; he remained one of the most treasured gifts from God Sara ever held and smothered with kisses.

Dyane rubbed the back of her own neck and then her arms. She didn't feel strong enough for this and didn't want her sister to leave her blue-eyed nephew. Holding her breath and bursting at the seams to cry out to God with a loud why of her own, she reached for Sara again, turned her head, and rested it upon Sara's thin shoulder. Dyane didn't want Sara to leave her either, especially when they had grown so close. Crying, holding, and comforting each other made time stand still. She relished the fact that Sara experienced the blessing of loving her nephew Cullen over the first year and a half of his life. Dyane's mind then filled with a list of shared memories all their own; Sara talking to her big baby belly, the intoxicated appearance on Sara's face after meeting Cullen for the first time, Sara's greeting and cuddling Cullen every morning for the four months they lived together, Sara showing him off to every friend at the hospital and to all of her nurses and doctors, and their vivacious game of Duck, Duck, Goose on the front lawn. She hoped, somewhere in the archive of his memory, he'd remember Sara and how much she loved him as her own. Dyane observed Sara allow the grief to rip at her heart and begin the process she once resisted. Empathizing with her pain, Dyane felt every ounce of strength squeeze from her reddening eyes. In Sara's last step of resistance, both of them allowed themselves to embrace the pain and the helplessness. By putting words to the sorrow together, they proceeded to let go of the attachments Sara's hands still held within her world.

In the days and weeks that followed, Dyane noted Sara asking for far less and seeking opportunities to give more of herself away to others. She noticed her offering more time to her family and friends, using her gifts to bless others, and planting the seeds of Christ's love with strangers. During these summer and fall months, Dyane not only felt proud of her sister for filling in as a teller at a local bank with her close friend Leigh but humbled by Sara's renewed acceptance and engagement with the life she still had left.

Chapter 16

An Inexpressible Joy

As soon as the red light on top of the camera illuminated, Sara cleared her throat and swallowed hard. The warmth of the lights upon the stage reflected the perspiration gathering above her lip.

"Welcome again to *Faith 20*. Today, I'm interviewing a very, very special person. Her name is Sarah Schreck, and Sara Schreck has terminal cancer. She has decided to refuse any more treatments for this cancer. She's a young woman of eighteen years of age, and she's been dealing with this for a little more than three years. She is one of my heroes, and I think that she will be one of yours after you hear her talk today. I think people like us need to listen to a young woman like this who knows things about life; some people never learn.

What was it like when you were fifteen when you were first diagnosed with cancer, and of course you were younger then, so you weren't really as mature as you are now, but how did that strike you when that happened?" Dr. Nederhood asked.

Sara enjoyed the familiar question and felt at ease. Her eyes fixed on Dr. Nederhood's mouth to make sure she understood what he asked.

"Well, whenever I was a freshman, I was very skinny and, and stuff like that, and I had started to notice changes in my body, and it made my self-esteem become very low. Umm, I was starting to gain weight; it wasn't a weight from eating, umm, so I went on this crash diet, as every typical teen would do. I tried to exercise, but it wasn't coming off," Sara said.

His eyes widened, and she settled back a little more into the comfortable orange chair that held her.

"Oh, my," stated Dr. Nederhood.

"And umm, it was really hard," said Sara.

"Yea, when they actually diagnosed your cancer, you gave me the name a little while ago, and I wouldn't dare try to repeat it because I simply couldn't keep it all straight. But did they know what it was right away when they began to actually give you a workup and so forth? Or did it take them a while to actually figure out what it was?" asked Dr. Nederhood.

"Umm, I think, I think they knew what it was. It was called Adrenal Cortical Carcinoma, and they said it was very rare, found one in two million," replied Sara.

"And for your age group especially, I understand it was very rare," Dr. Nederhood stated.

"Yes, yes," replied Sara.

"And so they did find it out quite early on, and then, they tried to treat it, and I understand that a lot of the treatments were experimental. Is that true?" Asked Dr. Nederhood.

Sara nodded, but her thoughts felt a little foggy.

"Yes, very experimental. Because it was so rare, nothing was written in books, so my doctor, I just kind of let him, or the Lord led him, and gave me two, two, two, and a half extra years of life," Sara replied.

She began to feel like her words stumbled out of her mouth. Her drying tongue grew distracting.

"Two and a half extra years of life because of what he—?"

"Yes," replied Sara.

"You were in one of our big teaching hospitals here in Chicago. Saint Luke's Presbyterian hospital?

"Rush," Sara stated.

"Rush, Saint Luke's Presbyterian. That's got all those names; it's all connected, but it's a teaching hospital, and I'm sure they took a great interest in your illness. Now, you became a Christian when you were about nine years of age, right? And were baptized when you were nine years of age? And you thought, my, this is wonderful to be Christian, but I'm sure since you've had this, this disease, your experience of Christ has changed. Would that be true?" Dr. Nederhood asked.

"Very much so," Sara replied.

"Can you explain that? What happens when a young person like yourself has to deal with this, and you begin to think about Christ another way?" asked Nederhood.

"When I was baptized, I really didn't know very much about it, and I started to grow. I went to a public grade school, and with my sisters being older, I noticed their examples, being an example of them. And, umm, I just kind of grew from there. But then, when I found out I was diagnosed, I just, I just prayed about it and decided, well, this is what the Lord wants me to do, and just decided to lean on Him. And it helped so much. They only thought I had six months to live,"

Sara stated.

Dr. Nederhood's eyes widened, causing his forehead to wrinkle.

"Really? When that happens, isn't it true that you pray differently than you ever did before? Was that true in your life?" He asked.

"Yes," Sara replied.

"With greater intensity?" Dr. Nederhood asked.

"Yes, very much so," Sara stated.

"Very, very much so. And you would then see two and a half years more. It's been about two and a half years since you were diagnosed, actually?" He inquired.

"Well, I was diagnosed in January, but I noticed changes in September," Sara replied.

"Okay, and how long do you think you still have? Do you have any idea?" Dr. Nederhood asked.

"I have no idea; I have no idea," Sara replied.

"What really caused you to finally come to the point to say, look, no more treatment? I mean, this is enough. How much treatment did you have? And then, what really was your treatment?" Dr. Nederhood asked.

Sara tried to sort out the questions and timeline in her head before she explained.

"I had a surgery this past, umm, early in the year, and I umm, had just waited it out. I decided the Lord was calling me home. I just, I couldn't, I didn't know, I couldn't put my finger on it. And, you know, I've been trying to witness to people, and I just really felt, I've been praying about it for so long. It wasn't a snap decision, and I decided that this is what the Lord wanted me to do," stated Sara.

"And I understand that when you were class graduated when you graduated from Illiana Christian High School be- cause that's ultimately where you went to school, you gave a little talk to your class, the largest group you ever talk- ed to. And what were some of the things that you said to these young people that you were graduating with? When you knew that they were going forward, and most of them would live longer than you would, and you were going to be with the Lord, what did you say to them?" Inquired Dr. Nederhood.

"Well, at that point, I didn't really know what my decision was going to be, and I didn't know what the Lord had in store for me. But umm, one of my favorite sayings is that I noticed once on a t-shirt—live like you'll die tomorrow, die like you'll live forever, and I told them that just to really focus on what's really important. To experience life and to not make things bigger than what they seem. To just try to pray about it and lean on the Lord. He won't give you anything more than He can handle," said Sara.

"Live today as if you were going to die tomorrow, now that makes every day a special gift of God, doesn't it? And every day, a very sweet and wonderful experience. What are your days like now?" He asked.

"Hmm, well, it depends; I wake up, and it's around how I feel. I go to work; it depends on how I feel, to see if I am able to go to work. When I can, I take morphine now. I don't take it every day, and sometimes it makes me groggy. So work,

I'm really blessed with a great workplace because they tell me when I get tired, I can go home. Like if I can't come in, it's okay," Sara said.

"What do you do at your work?" Dr. Nederhood asked.

"Well, umm, I was filing for a while, but I can't do that anymore. So, they're training me as a teller, and now I'm getting pretty good at that. I love it," Sara said.

Her smile brightened, and blue eyes sparkled as she remembered those she worked with, those she met, and the things she did at the bank.

"As a teller, you're meeting people all the time?" he asked.

"Yes," Sara replied.

"So, if I come into that bank, maybe you can help me out? So, what's the name of it?" Dr. Nederhood asked.

"First Savings and Loan of South Holland," she said.

"And that's a community right next to mine, so that'd be a good place to come and see you sometime, and you'll be working there. Now, every day is very important. You also mentioned something about when we think about this, that we shouldn't make little things into big things every day. That's also a big part of the picture. I mean when people don't get along with one another and they, I guess you'd say, they fight together sometimes. That doesn't make much sense when you're in the kind of situation you're in, does it?"

"Right," Sara said.

"It's something where you have to deal with those things a little bit differently. You have a family, tell me about your parents, and you mentioned your sisters are older than you?"

"Yes," Sara said.

"What sort of family do you have?" He asked.

"I have a very large family; our family has always been close, which is awesome," Sara said.

"Are you the youngest?"

Sara paused and considered the question, wondering what he meant.

"Out of the whole family?" Sara asked.

"Yes, out of your immediate family, are you the youngest?" Dr. Nederhood inquired.

"Yes, I'm the youngest. Out of my whole entire family, on my mother's side, we are all very close, and this has just even brought us even closer. And umm, the Lord has really blessed me," she stated.

"And He's blessed your family too, through all of this?" He asked.

"Oh, definitely, definitely," Sara agreed.

"What's it done to your family? How would you describe that?" Dr. Nederhood inquired.

"Umm, I think we've all just become spiritually motivated, and umm, we've become Christians and have been a witness to other people. My cousins have written papers about me; it's really touched me," Sara said.

"Yes, well, I know churches that are watching your progress. I know the church I go to, we get a sheet that tells us how you doing and what's happening. We're all praying. I think one of the things this does, it just draws people together in prayer in a very special way," He stated.

"Definitely," Sara said.

"Prayer gets to be really the only language that makes any sense, doesn't it, when you're in a situation like this?" Dr. Nederhood asked.

"Especially when it's personal with the Lord," Sara stated.

Dr. Nederhood nodded.

"That's right. Tell me about your relationship to the Lord; how do you experience the presence of Jesus Christ in your life now? As you think about the fact, you know, let me just say this, the Apostle Peter says about Jesus, you have not seen Him, but you love Him. And even though you haven't seen Him, you believe in Him, and you're filled with an inexpressible joy. A great joy because you're receiving the salvation of your souls. We haven't seen Jesus. How do you experience Jesus, as you know you're getting closer to seeing Him?" He inquired.

Sara understood the weight of his question and remembered how her relationship with Jesus changed since the diagnosis.

"Well, I just know that, you know, humbling yourself is

273

so important, and that's what we have to do. I personally—I had to humble myself to Him and let Him take over. I don't know," Sara replied.

A soft smile lit her face, hoping he and his listeners understood the words weren't coming easily. She knew she used to hold on to everything and everyone so tight. She felt uncertain in this moment, how to put everything about her personal relationship with Jesus into words. If he asked, she'd tell him she just took one day at a time in her walk with Him. She trusted Jesus, and she knew He helped her.

"It has to be a complete surrender," Dr. Nederhood agreed.

"Right, definitely. And I'm just praying to Him," she said.

"And you mentioned that when they confronted you with the possibility of maybe having even more chemotherapy, that you decided that maybe that wasn't a thing to do. And maybe He was calling you home. What does that mean to you when you think of Christ calling you home? What kind of home do you visualize? What do you think about that? You said to your friends that you have to live today as if you were going to die tomorrow, and you have to die as if you're going to live forever. Let's talk about that living forever side of this little bit," Dr. Nederhood stated.

An Inexpressible Joy

"Well, I've been reading about heaven a lot. One of my great friends has given me a book, it's a children's book, and it says how the Lord has prepared a place for me or prepared a room for me. My room has always been very important. I used to think that the Lord is, umm, is just preparing for me. I get to go and see this awesome God that has created so much. And in a way, I'm kind of excited. I know it's kind of hard uh—scary," Sara said.

"I know it's hard to leave your family, I'm sure," he stated.

Sara sat up a little straighter in her seat and her eyes danced.

"Yes, but I know that they're right behind me because I know that they all know the Lord. So, that part doesn't scare me; it's just the suffering part. It scares me a little bit. But they said that they're going to take care of it with pain medication, so the Lord's going to take care of me," stated Sara.

Sara nodded her head, and an unexplainable peace filled her.

"And take you through that," he agreed.

"Yes," Sara stated.

Her lips then curved upward at hearing he understood everything she said.

"Now you mentioned that this illness that you have is very, very rare. Do you ever try to figure out why it is that *you* had this and someone else didn't? How do you try to handle that puzzle? Does that ever puzzle you? Do you ever wonder about that?" inquired Dr. Nederhood.

Sara offered a slight chuckled, glanced downward, and brushed her slacks with her hand.

"So, it's funny you say it 'cause umm, like the first two years I had cancer, I never tried to ask why, because I tried to, you know, to focus on the Lord and say, *okay Lord, if this is what, you know, this is what you have planned for me.* But lately, because I've been in more pain, I recently asked the Lord, *why me?* And it was the hardest thing I've ever had to say.

"For two years, you didn't say it?" Dr. Nederhood asked.

"Right, and when I did, I was up all night crying. Saying *Lord, please forgive me,* because He says, you know, to surrender all your problems to me," Sara stated.

"Right and cast all your burdens on Him, and He'll take care of you. And how have you dealt with that question? You mentioned, first of all, when you start to ask it, it made you almost ashamed to ask it. But have you had any answers to it?" He asked.

"Yes, actually, that same day. My girlfriend called me up and told me about this program. And then, I got calls from other churches that wanted me to give some testimonies. So, I was talking to my sister, and I said *I'm never asking why again*," Sara said.

She shook her head, smiling.

"Well, it's true that a person like yourself, you know, you are a young person of eighteen years of age, but you are a special prophetess for us. Because God has been working so marvelously in your life, and he's giving you faith. And you've been able to handle this in a faith-filled way. We need to hear from your lips what it's like to go through this because there are just all kinds of people who ask these questions, and they don't have any answers. Let me ask you another question. When you think about dying, when I think about my death, and so forth, I think about meeting Jesus, meeting God. He's going to be our judge, right? He's a judge too. How do you handle your sins? You're a sinner, I suppose, aren't you?" He asked.

"Yes, definitely," Sara said.

"You look perfect to me today, but I mean like, everyone else, what do you think about when you think about the sins you've committed? In the fact that you're going to be meeting Christ?" Dr. Nederhood asked.

"Well, the Lord asks us to tell Him our problems, and I asked Him to please forgive me. And, He promises He will wipe away all our sins. Just like that," she stated.

"Our sins are gone, aren't they?" he asked.

"Yes, and that's what's so neat about God. It amazes me," Sara said.

Sara nodded in agreement, feeling excitement pulse through her body and cheeks warm.

"Right, and when you appear before Him, you are actually going to be dressed in Jesus clothing, aren't you? You're going to wear his righteousness, and we're always very concerned about what we wear. It'll be great to wear the righteousness that He gives. Are there any special, you know as Christians we sing about heaven, we sing about Golden streets and so forth. Is there any special imagery or any special ideas, or concepts about heaven, that particularly delight you and fill you with anticipation as you think about the fact that you're going to be there very soon?" He asked.

Sara gazed upward, recalling and imagining heaven.

"Umm, I know there will be lots of light, and there'll be no darkness in heaven. I was at my church, and there was a sermon that, and I thought that was just so neat because darkness kind of contributes to evil. There's going to be lots of light, and lots of happiness, and no more sadness, and no more suffering and fear. We'll just be so busy thinking of other things and talking with the Lord. We're just not going to worry about anything," Sara stated.

"Do you have any dear ones who've gone on before are there already, like a grandmother or grandfather?" Dr. Nederhood asked.

"Yes, I have had a grandma and a grandpa," Sara replied.

"Alright, and what do you think? Do you think we will recognize our loved ones in heaven?

"Umm, I don't know, that's one of those questions I have to ask the Lord," Sara said.

Sara giggled and tilted her head.

"Well, may I tell you what I think?" He asked.

Sara's interest peaked.

"Sure," Sara replied.

"I think we surely will. In fact, I heard someone ask one time, 'do you think we will really recognize the people that we loved on earth? Will we recognize the people in heaven and know them?' I heard this answer, and I thought it was very good, you know, we're going to know them better than we ever knew them before, because in this world we always have little barriers between ourselves. You know, we don't always reveal ourselves completely to other people, but there we will know each other more fully than we have here. So, you're gonna have to find that out, but that's the great hope I have. You know, we want to see Jesus someday, very much to see Jesus, but Jesus has given us so many wonderful family members and so many friends in this world. It's good to know that we're going to see them too; if they believe in Jesus, you know, we'll get to see them.

Now, you're looking at me right now, but I want you to use your imagination a minute and just forget that you're looking at me and just think about the fact that all of a sudden, you're looking at a teenager. And that takes a lot of imagination when you look at me if you think you're looking at a teenager! But you just think of that, you're looking at a teenager on the streets of New York City or Los Angeles, and you have this opportunity to tell them exactly what they need to know about Jesus. What would you tell me in a case like that? If you were witnessing to me, in your situation, and I'm a young person. What would you want me to know?" Dr. Nederhood asked.

Sara's eyes tilted a little as she listened to his question and began to process the weight of the question out loud.

"I would just talk to them about the Lord, and umm, not necessarily overpower them, but just share my faith, plant a seed, and maybe the Lord will put someone else in their life. I'd just tell them that to live each day to the fullest, I can't say that enough, and trust in the Savior. Yes, trust in him," Sara said.

Sara's soft smile and tiring countenance seemed to touch Dr. Nederhood. He smiled in return, and their eyes locked as he concluded his interview.

"I want to thank you so very much for your bravery

and your courage, and I join your many friends in praising God for the marvelous faith that He's given to you. I'm so grateful that you've been willing to share your testimony with the people who watch *Faith 20*, and I know that many hearts have been touched. I know that because of this program, there's going to be just thousands and maybe millions of people who are going to be praying for you in the months and weeks ahead, that God is going to be with you as you go through that very, very, mysterious experience of leaving this world and going to the next one come. I want to tell you something when you close your eyes in this world, you're going to look right into the face of Jesus Christ. You know that, don't you? God bless you, Sara. Thank you for being here."

Dr. Nederhood's eyes then met the screen before him.

"This is the very wonderful person we talked to today, and I hope her testimony has touched your heart because this is all there is, nothing more to hold onto except Jesus. Jesus is our only hope and when you trust in Christ, when you turn your life over to Him, confess your sins, and you ask the Holy Spirit into your heart, this God makes you immortal, and death will never touch you. That's what Jesus said; I am the resurrection and the life he who believes in me, though He dies yet shall He live. It's impossible to be separated. You know that's what this book talks about; hope in the face of death, if you'd like to have a copy of it, will send you one."

As the red light on the camera before her faded, Sara breathed a sigh of relief. Dr. Nederhood reached out his hand and shook hers. His kindness put Sara's building uncertainty about the interview at ease.

"Thank you, dear, thank you for being with us today," he said.

"You're welcome, thank you," Sara replied.

She followed him towards her mom and sisters in the shadowed wings of the staging area. As they affirmed the great job she did, smiled, and helped her get her coat on, she bit the inside of her cheek, wondering if her words might encourage anyone. Her legs felt weak beneath her as she zipped up her coat, slid her gloves over her slender fingers, and placed a knit cap upon her head. She took a deep breath and stepped forward, following the crowd toward the exit. A chill met her as the door opened, sucked the warm air out of the building, and she interlocked her arms with her mom. Gazing to the left, she noticed the Trinity Christian College campus in the distance and then hid her face behind a whipping scarf. Relief set in after shutting the heavy car door.

She unwrapped her face as they pulled out of the lot, feeling satisfied, and rested her chin upon her gloved fist. As the traffic increased, she knew in her spirit; she accomplished what God had wanted her to do.

Chapter 17

Come Closer

All year Sara and Dyane shared a private, ongoing banter.

"You better not die on my birthday," Dyane stated.

Clothing their kidding in laughter, the sisters teased, making light of her request. In late October, as brittle brown leaves swirled outside and just a week before Dyane's twenty-fourth birthday, Sara assured Dyane over and over again. What some might consider a morbid joke, Dyane and Sara didn't—instead, they enjoyed razzing each other over something Dyane really hoped her sister had some say in. However, while funny to them, they took great care not to discuss it in public, as some might misunderstand.

Maribeth along with her closest Rush hospital nurses, all threw a Halloween party in Sara's honor the week prior to Dyane's birthday on Tuesday, October 31st. Dyane knew Sara didn't have the heart to tell them she didn't celebrate the day but instead focused on her great love for each of them and the opportunity she held. A few more friends joined in the gathering, as well as Sara's family. The nurses planned a night of pumpkin carving, face painting, picture taking, and lots of eating.

Dyane arrived at the house later in the evening to find Sara looking well other than the deep shadowed circles surrounding her eyes. Snuggling up next to each other, their mom took a photograph at the kitchen counter. Midway through Sara's illness, both Dyane and Sara realized how few pictures they took together alone. During moments like these, they purposed to take many photos together to make up for the lost time.

The party that night revealed Sara's waning determination and strength. In spite of how she felt, Dyane understood Sara's desire to make the most of every moment with the nurse friends she once spent so much time with at the hospital. She watched her make every effort to enjoy her party, regardless of her need for rest. Dyane noticed her physical exhaustion, her water retention, and her moving with great pain that night. However, regardless of Sara's unspoken struggles, Dyane took note of the loving responses to her friends. With faces painted and a generous determination to give, everyone achieved a memorable night with Sara.

Come Closer

The next morning, even though she felt worn over the previous night's activities, Sara awoke with a renewed vigor from a lengthy night's rest. She readied herself for a lady's day out with her grandma, mom, both sisters, and her nephew Cullen. They prepared for Sara's appointment at the funeral home and an upbeat lunch out.

Sara primped in front of a mirror and sat on the floor dressed in one of her most stylish outfits. From behind, Dyane watched over Cullen as he toddled up to his Auntie Sara's side and plopped himself upon the floor right next to her. He fixated upon her face, down at the compact where she dipped her brush, and in awe watched his auntie drift the soft bristles on her face. Almost two years old, Cullen asked her multiple times—

"Whaaat thiiis? Whaaat thiiis?"

Sara grinned down at him with affection. As she took the time to describe every item in her make-up bag, as well as every step of her make-up routine to her attentive nephew, Dyane, Elizabeth, and their mom amused themselves behind the camera.

After lunch, Dyane absorbed every surrealistic moment at the funeral home. She also struggled between grief over where she sat and the process by which she felt joy for her sister. Sara radiated pleasure while discussing her goals with the funeral director. Sara brought a written list with her, detailing each one of her future funeral wishes. However, every time she mentioned her personal preferences, her comments caused the funeral home director to pause. Dyane found the exchange quite entertaining and snickered behind the pamphlet she held between her fingers. It seemed he didn't have much interaction with his living casket customers, not to mention a young woman like Sara Schreck.

Once they entered the casket room, Sara peered at each casket carefully. She observed and inspected every carving, each inlay of fabric, each hue, hinge, and every shade of wood grain. Sara asked the salesman specific questions and narrowed her choices to only a few. At the remembrance of her outfit selection for her special day, she made a final choice. Dyane imagined the casket's interior upholstery beautifully complimenting Sara's pre-chosen dress. Once Sara's decided, the finished casket, with all of the extras, totaled over $5,000, Dyane saw Susan swallow, raise her eyebrows, and bend over the desk to write a check.

"This is your new car," her mother stated.

Her mother's playful tone enlivened Sara's smile. The deep mahogany exterior and gathered cream moray taffeta fabric reflected Sara's elegant taste. Regardless of traditional funeral home experiences, everyone had a wonderful time, hopped into the car, and shared the kind of laughter over lunch of any family preparing for a party.

In the same way, Joseph and Dyane planned their wedding celebration years before, Sara designed her funeral, and she didn't miss a detail. Her written list contained bullet points for all involved to follow:

- What I'm wearing—Mom's off-white wedding dress.

- The visitation and service—Deer Creek Christian Church, University Park, IL

- Pall Bearers—Neil (brother-in-law), Joseph (brother-in-law), Matt (first cousin), Allen (first cousin), Matthew (friend and youth minister at Deer Creek).

- I want to be cremated.

- Worship songs by the Deer Creek Band—"Step By Step," "Seek Ye First," "As The Deer," "My God Is An Awesome God," "More Precious Than Silver,"

"Hero" (Special Music), "Thank You," "Watch The Lamb," and "If You Could See Me Now."

- Instruments—Mr. Greis—trumpet.

- Sign Language—Jude G.—whole service.

- Flowers—calla lilies—white and yellow, and pink roses.

- Casket—Deep mahogany with white moray taffeta.

- Favorite verses to be read:

Philippians 4:12-13,

I know what it is to be in need, and I know what it is to have plenty. I have learned the secret of being content in any and every sit-uation, whether well fed or hungry, whether living in plenty or in want. I can do all things through Him who gives me strength.

John 14:6-7,

Jesus answered, "I am the way and the truth and the life. No one comes to the Father

290

except through me. If you really know me, you will know my Father as well. From now on, you do know him and have seen him."

First Corinthians 15:54-57,

When the perishable has been clothed with the imperishable, and the mortal with immortality, then the saying that is written will come true: "Death has been swallowed up in victory." "Where, O death, is your victory? Where, O death, is your sting?" The sting of death is sin and the power of sin is the law. But thanks be to God! He gives us the victory through our Lord Jesus Christ.

Romans 5:1-5,

Therefore, since we have been justified through faith, we have peace with God through our Lord Jesus Christ, through whom we have gained access by faith into this grace in which we now stand. And we boast in the hope of the glory of God. Not only so but we also glory in our sufferings, because we know that suffering produces perseverance; perseverance, char-

acter; and character, hope. And hope does not put us to shame, because God's love has been poured out into our hearts through the Holy Spirit, who has been given to us.

- Pastors for service—Earl Ferguson and Matthew Rogers

- Donations instead of flowers: Deer Creek Christian School and Illiana Christian High School

- Poem—Cheryl Frit

- Last song— "If You Could See Me Now"

From the dress to officiating ministers for the service, the flowers, the music, and even a soloist—Dyane knew Sara's extensive preparation led to feelings of great peace for everyone.

***

Dyane had once heard about people who prepared to pass away, so the next day over breakfast, she hesitated only for a moment before she brought up the things pressing upon her mind.

"You know, if you ever feel like it's time to call everyone to say goodbye, I want you to tell me, okay? I'd let everyone know for you," she said.

Dyane didn't worry about anyone overhearing or thinking their weighty conversation too casual over breakfast, and neither did Sara. They spoke about many things like this and took each other seriously when one or the other spoke. Sara appeared calm and assured by Dyane's question. She trusted Sara to tell her if the question weighed heavy or remained too much to bear. Sara's thoughtful reply instead reassured Dyane; Sara trusted her in return.

With all of her future plans in mind, all looming obstacles she overcame behind her, and the simple moments before Sara with family—Dyane relished Sara's plan to slow down and be in the moment. Dyane's birthday celebration drew near in a matter of days, and Sara still held to the promise she made to her oldest sister. Balloons needed blowing up, gifts needed wrapping, a birthday dessert needed baking, and Sara shuffled around the house as a key part of it all.

Dyane set her attention on Cullen climbing up the playroom stairs to line up his racecars. She hovered by the doorway and heard Sara and their mom laugh in the downstairs kitchen over a love note Jim wrote to Susan that morning. Dyane chuckled and noticed Sara work up a dramatic gag with her finger to provoke Susan to laughter. She longed to remember moments like these, the enjoyment of watching Cullen play in the playroom she grew up playing in, the playfulness with their mom, and giggles around the kitchen counter that drew a crowd. Resolved to not forget, she decided no birthday gift compared to the thrill those picturesque family memories brought her.

***

On November 3rd, early in the day, Friday, Dyane moved about Sara's room, helping her straighten bedding and hang up a few pieces of clothing. Sara expressed her appreciation for the help and settled into her bed to rest for a while. Conversations between Susan and Grandma Irene over Dyane's birthday dinner continued down in the kitchen, and Dyane felt happy to make herself scarce. Using Cullen's naptime to hang out with Sara felt productive and relaxing. As Dyane hummed to the music Sara played on her CD player, she hung the last of Sara's clean laundry on her closet rod. Sara spoke to Dyane's back.

"Dyane, it's time," Sara stated.

"*It's time?*" Dyane questioned.

Come Closer

As if in a dream, Dyane mulled over the statement. Sara looked great, remained in high spirits, and even appeared energized. However, Sara confided in her sister, as Dyane asked her to just a few days before. Sara's sincere, soft gaze spoke like nothing before. Dyane stood stunned for a moment and then resolved to follow through with her promise to call everyone to Sara's side.

Amidst the uncertainty of some, Dyane and her mother made phone calls to family and Sara's closest friends. They asked each one to come to their home, without appointment, just a simple invitation to come to spend time with Sara. In a steady stream, almost every person on Sara's list arrived throughout the day. Crowding into Sara's bedroom, they goofed around near her bedside together and visited.

Evening fell early that chilled November evening. After most friends went home for the night, more family members slipped into Jim and Susan's home to see Sara after work. Some drove over two hours, and a few brought their overnight bags even though they lived just twenty minutes away. Dyane glanced in Sara's direction, smiling as she proceeded to pile her unopened birthday gifts next to Sara's bed on a table. With everyone squeezing into her bedroom, the tune of "Happy Birthday" rang out prior to watching Dyane open her birthday gifts. Her face reddened as she unwrapped a new winter coat from her grandmother, to which Sara beamed and gently clapped her hands.

The whirlwind day became something Dyane never expected, and not one person wanted to leave Sara's side. It grew late, and many of them forgot to make the birthday dinner. Susan felt embarrassed and weary from all the day's activities and asked Dyane if she minded having fast food. Grateful, she, as well as everyone else, welcomed the idea of anything after such a lengthy day. After their mom tucked Sara into bed for the night, the party resumed downstairs, and everyone clustered around the kitchen counter.

Lightheadedness swept over Dyane just before her stepdad returned from the dinner run. Once she received the wrapped warm beef and cheese sandwich, Dyane peeled back the paper and sank her teeth into it. About halfway through, she looked down at the rest of her meal and noticed something unusual. Dyane stood, twisting her sandwich under the overhead kitchen light, and saw what she feared, the remainder of her bun covered in a greenish hue of mold. Her stomach sank, and she rewrapped the foiled paper around it again without a word. Her heart raced, and she closed her eyes and breathed deep to settle her heart rate. What might have thrown Dyane into a fit of panic just a day before prompted Dyane to feel something far different. She remembered the day's events, the last few years of memories, and Sara asleep upstairs folded into the blankets upon her bed. She exhaled with indifference and shrugged her shoulders.

"In the grand scheme of things—it really doesn't matter," Dyane stated.

No, it didn't. The issue caved in importance that evening, yet it remained a great tale for future fits of family laughter.

Desiring to give her mom and stepdad a break that evening, Elizabeth and Dyane made and fluffed their beds upon the floor of Sara's room while she slept. Their sleepover together that night almost held a feeling of urgency; both of them slept light, barely dreaming, and woke often throughout the night. Sara also awoke so early; darkness still filled her bedroom. She groaned. Once the sisters heard her, they flung off their covers and rushed to her bedside. Sara, unable to hear their questioning or read their lips in the dark, attempted with little success to sit up taller. Both girls helped by shifting her legs to the side of the bed, where they hung limp. As Elizabeth and Dyane began to guide Sara off the bed towards the portable commode, they quickly realized her inability to communicate or stand alone in her weakness. Sara dropped downward, sliding off of the edge of the mattress, and they noticed the absence of strength in her legs to help them as they struggled to guide her. It took every bit of muscle they shared to hoist Sara by themselves and tend to her needs without dropping her onto the carpeting. Dyane prayed for a miracle, and at that moment–*God, help us–please!* Miraculous strength came as they lifted her off of the toilet seat. Once they tipped back her into the bed, they covered her up well. Neither of them spoke again before sunrise but heard the sighs and deep breaths from the other. Dyane wiped at the sweat beading up on her forehead. As she lay upon the blankets next to Elizabeth, she practiced calm, lengthy breathing to lead her into sleep again.

Not long before the sun rose and Elizabeth and Dyane woke again to discover Sara in a coma-like state. Dyane's pulse quickened. Elizabeth ran for their mother, and a few came running upstairs. Her stepdad's nose flared, and Susan moaned. Their mom placed her hand upon Sara's forehead and called to Sara with a soft voice. Dyane's heart beat fast, and her lips tingled. Joseph's slanted glance toward her made her heart ache all the more. Without question, it remained a hundred and eighty-degree change from the day before.

In their nervousness, they scattered. Susan began to place phone calls to Sara's hospice nurses, including her closest nurse Maribeth from the upstairs kitchen, and their Grandma Irene called more family as well.

Everyone stayed out of Susan and Jim's way, tending to their own needs. Relieved, Dyane witnessed church family members and neighbors dropping off enough food and paper goods to her parents to last them for weeks, and Susan expressed her gratefulness in between phone calls and running up and down the stairs.

As the last of their relatives hung their coats on the coat rack in the foyer, everyone agreed; no one wanted to leave the house that weekend. Ideas flowed into Dyane's mind as to how to keep her sister comfortable and at peace with so much activity going on downstairs. She searched her sister's closet for soft instrumental hymns to play next to her bedside. She hoped it comforted her. At different points throughout the day, Dyane peeked in where Sara lay alone in her bedroom.

Earlier in the afternoon, Elizabeth and Dyane stole a few moments with their sister to spread a flowering herb-scented lotion upon Sara's arms and legs. Neither spoke as the instrumental hymns played. In a slow and gentle glide, they smoothed their slathered hands over her skin, and the sweet scent filled their noses as well as the room. Sara's favorite fragrance wrapped her as if in a soft floral blanket. Losing track of time, their gift of love compelled them to act and minister to their little sister in a way only they knew how. Elizabeth and Dyane reminded Sara of their love through touch, through her favorite scent, and by spending those sacred moments by her side. Nothing else mattered to them—*nothing*.

After they finished, Dyane twisted the cap closed on the lotion bottle as Elizabeth and their mom slowly gathered the collection of items they needed to bring back downstairs with them. They left Sara's room in silence while Sara laid upon her bed without movement. Dyane remained, resetting the cassette tape of light instrumental praise music. Soft musical notes floated upon the air and whispered comforting familiar tunes for everyone to enjoy. Dyane hesitated at the doorway, glanced backward toward Sara, and then felt great uncertainty about leaving the room. She felt a headache coming on, as well as a deepening feeling of abandonment sinking into her core.

The moments slipped by with a slow stillness like nothing they ever experienced before. As if everyone held their breath in unison, they watched Sara that evening. Jim and

Susan, Dyane and Joseph, Elizabeth and Neil, their aunts, uncles, cousins, their husbands, and a few close friends stood in Sara's bedroom. Cullen snuggled with Dyane while he rested on her hip in his footie jammies. Their conversations reduced to whispers. They watched her chest rise and fall; every breath flowed in and poured out. Dyane noticed at different points, even her own breathing timed well with her sister's inhales and exhales. Bending low, Dyane decided to whisper into her sister's ear.

"Let us know if you see angels…"

But Sara didn't stir. No one left her bedside, yet some repositioned her blankets and sat upon them. Some huddled in a corner, and some folded their arms and leaned upon her dresser.

Dyane felt unsettled by Sara's greyed appearance, lack of response towards them earlier that day and throughout the afternoon. She closed her eyes and released a calming breath. The complete turn of events summoned closer friends and family back together to surrounded Sara. They all watched her for hours, but her eyes remained shut, and she laid still and silent. Not long after the clock struck four-thirty, most exited the room to find dinner, and a few of the women stayed behind. Then, without any warning, Sara mumbled gruff words no one in the room understood.

"Honey, what did you say?" Sara's mother, Susan, asked.

Sara then repeated the unexpected words.

"Water, water…"

Susan, trembling, tried to give her daughter water, but Sara pushed it away with her hand all while her eyes remained closed. At that moment, they stirred up, anxiously trying to solve the mystery before them. Why she said *water, water,* and then pushed the glass of water away, they didn't know.

Aunt Judy brightened and remembered a book she once read about someone who died and came back to life. The author spoke about going to heaven and hearing the sounds of water. Dyane's face flushed while wondering how her sister, with severe hearing loss, heard the sounds of water. They continued to ask Sara questions, hoping to draw a response, but she didn't. She didn't respond again to anything they asked, and Dyane mulled over what those alarming moments meant. They looked at each other as she lay there unmoving again, like the moments prior. Then, some embraced as the women's spirits stirred with excitement. Sara communicated with them, and regardless of how short-lived, Dyane's heart raced. They stood waiting, even more alert than before—ready to listen and respond to anything else she might say. A little while later, Sara's eyes opened full and wide. Without words, she raised her arms, stretched out her hands, and lifted them both up and angled toward the end of her bed. She reached—staring as if taking hold of someone's hand, and the women held their breaths. They didn't know what to say or do. In mere seconds, the moment ended, her eyes closed, and her arms collapsed toward the bed next to her body. Again, she became quiet and still. Among the soft cries and hugs surrounding Dyane, she proceeded to close her eyes also, allowing the tears brimming them to pour down her cheeks. In the silence, she prayed, *Father, thank you for allowing me to be here for this moment—thank you for capturing our attention...*

Chapter 18

Promises Kept

As the sun began to set, the lights in Sara's bedroom glowed warm and golden than earlier that day. No movements like what they saw in the late afternoon happened again, but they all continued to watch Sara with hope. Because of the growing crowd within Sara's bedroom, as the evening progressed, places to sit grew scarce. Most stood along the dresser and leaned upon the footboard of Sara's bed, waiting for her to say or do something again. As more arrived, they took their places within the remaining corners of Sara's bedroom. The volume grew, and many carried on in conversation and laughter as if they stood down in the kitchen. No one gave it a second thought because if Sara awakened, they didn't want her to feel left out.

Cullen toddled around his Auntie Sara's room, and Dyane hesitated to put him to bed at his normal bedtime hour. He didn't understand why his auntie laid in bed and did not talk or play with him like she always did. Every now and then, he drew near to her bedside, lifted up on the edge of Sara's bed sheet, and checked on her. On his last toddle into the room, though, his grandma lifted him up next to Sara's face.

"Give Auntie a kiss goodnight," she said.

Cullen kissed her, and she didn't even stir a little bit. Dyane continued to sit next to Sara by her headboard while Joseph put him to bed for the night.

Not long afterward, Sara began to groan with more volume than ever before. Those on the bed leaned a bit closer, and those on along the perimeter of the room rushed towards the bed in a panic.

"What is it, baby? What do you need?" her mother questioned. Sara didn't reply. Susan checked all around her bed, and after the men in the room turned their heads, she pulled her sheets backward.

"We need to change her bottom sheet," she stated.

Concern strained her voice. After collaboration, some of the women decided on the best idea, to tilt her body to the side with the highest of hope of remaking the bed with her in it. Dyane's armpits began to sweat. Sara grimaced in her sleep while the women scurried around and tried to turn her upper and lower body at the same time. Determined, they attempted to tip her to one side of the bed, but the effort proved to be pointless. It seemed to Dyane, their vain efforts without the men's help lacked the muscle they needed to pull off the sheet-changing maneuver. They felt helpless and uncertain of what to do next. The men in their family continued to create their own plan and put it into immediate action. A few options arose amongst them regarding the task at hand.

"Jim, you take that right top corner of the sheet, Joseph the other corner, and Neil this one?" Sara's uncle Thomas asked.

Anxiety and tension began to tighten Dyane's body. She glanced around the room and then helped prepare Sara for her travel by sheet to the carpet. Dyane scratched the back of her head, feeling a growing concern about the endeavor. While the guys teamed up along the bedside edges, the wrinkling fitted sheet gathered beneath her. Dyane scurried to the area where they planned to lay her down on the floor. Dyane's mom and her aunts prepared their plan to slip another sheet upon the bed as soon as the men lifted Sara off of the mattress.

"One, two, three…" they said.

Nodding in unison, they lifted her sagging body with all of their might. Loud, pain-filled groans like they had never heard before filled the air. Sara wailed as they carried and lowered her bent body nearer to the carpet where Dyane stood. She and her husband clung to each other, peering down upon Sara's body, curled underneath the curving puckered sheet. Some of them dropped to the ground to soothe her by touching Sara's head and feet. Dyane noticed her jammies pulling up on the backside, and she panicked. Blackened and purple bruises stretched behind her rib cage. Dyane thought back to the day before when Elizabeth helped her get Sara dressed; no sign of bruising appeared, and she raised a hand to her mouth. They all discussed the new bruising and realized Sara's body needed far more than they knew to do. Jim stepped away and called the hospice nurse. Then with even more concern and care, the remaining men lifted her back up to her clean bed, and she cried out with the same intensity. The ladies drew close again, tightening the circle around Sara's bed, covering her, desiring to warm her and make her more comfortable.

What seemed like only minutes later, Sara's eyes popped open wider than earlier in the day, and she gasped for breath. A rush of tingling shot through Dyane's fingers. Sara became frantic. Her mother and sister Elizabeth perched next to Sara's bedside, and Elizabeth proceeded to cry out. Not knowing why, Dyane watched Elizabeth leap off Sara's bed in alarm. At that moment, their mother grabbed Dyane's arm and yanked her towards her side, all while leaning in unison towards Sara's face. Gasp after alarming gasp—Sara looked through them as if they became tissue paper. Dyane's arms entangled around her mother's as hers clutched Sara's. Susan stiffened, and Dyane locked on Sara's gasping for breath. With widening saucer-like eyes and her mouth opened in terror—she fought for more air. Sobbing, Dyane realized she struggled to breathe herself. Elizabeth cried out behind her as everyone around them did the same, but Dyane deafened herself to every noise except her mother's words.

"It's okay, baby—" Her mother assured.

Susan, while consoling her daughter through her own blinding tears, cried out to Sara as if her little girl held back from drifting away.

"Go, home baby—go home…"

Dyane held her mother tight from behind while Susan continued to make the same plea to Sara over and over again. Dyane refused to take her eyes off of Sara's face. In a state of shock, she held her breath as she watched Sara's frightful expression fade into a still restful sleep. Bursting into tears,

Dyane bent closer to Susan while she agonized in tears of her own. Sara's mother reached over and closed Sara's eyes with the same gentle hand she extended upon her daughter's face in the recovery room. They grasped and clung to one another like life rings in an ocean of tears.

Dyane's husband held her shoulders, and she turned to him, burying her wet face into his shirt. Releasing him after she felt her courage return, she turned to view Sara's body again. She looked at it but didn't see her sister Sara there anymore. Everything that made Sara alive, fun, joyful, and beautiful left. Just to make sure, Dyane reached out her fingers and touched the skin of Sara's hand. Its smooth surface held a chill and felt stiff. Her body appeared like a shed cicada shell, void of her joyful spirit. Dyane sat there, stunned at what just happened, and just stared. She heard the discussion about calling their pastor Earl and the funeral home. The quiet conversations, nose-blowing, and the soft sobs behind her continued. It felt surreal. Just yesterday, they held Dyane's birthday party in the very room she sat in. A likeness of her baby sister laid still and quiet. In the briefest of moments, while Dyane merely blinked, someone in the room spoke about Sara's appearance. Feeling her eyes sting, Dyane rubbed them and refocused upon her sister's face. Something changed. Her lips, now raised at the corners, caused Dyane's laugh to burst in surprise.

"She's fixed her face," someone said.

"She left it there for us," her youngest cousin Brittany stated.

That's just like her, Dyane thought. And everyone agreed; that grin appeared after she passed away.

"That's just like Sara!" Grandma Irene exclaimed.

While a slight laughter rang out among the aunts, uncles, cousins, and a few friends throughout the room, Dyane remembered again Sara's magnetic personality, and determined not to forget it. Her sister never missed a detail in her life, and she knew for a fact that she wanted a soft grin frozen upon her face. Then, Dyane's breath caught, remembering a promise Sara kept to her alone. Sara didn't pass away on Dyane's birthday, and she clung to the memory as the best gift Sara and God ever gave her on Saturday, November 4th, 1995.

Chapter 19

Secrets

After a late and restless night of sleep at her parents' home and before heading downstairs in the morning, Dyane turned toward Sara's doorway. She leaned up against the doorjamb and scanned her darkened room. It sat lifeless now, still, and empty. Their long talks in her bedroom were over, no more foot massages, fashion shows, or sleepovers to enjoy. She swallowed down a lump within her throat, but its tightness still kept Dyane from gaining a deep enough breath. The day ahead of them called to her, promising to remain long, filled with preparations for Sara's well-planned funeral.

Later in the morning, Susan asked her daughters Elizabeth and Dyane to join her in the upstairs bathroom—their favorite meeting spot. They climbed the stairs close behind their mother, and after entering through the doorway, Susan spun around and handed each of them an envelope. She spoke in such soft tones that Dyane leaned in to hear her.

"Sara wanted me to give this to you girls," she said.

They tore at the glued flap and opened their own envelopes. Elizabeth and Dyane both noticed a row of bills tucked inside. They looked at their mother, confused.

"Sara wanted you to buy a new outfit for her funeral," she stated.

Her eyes sparkled, and she grinned light but mischievous. Speechless and weakened, they stepped toward their mother, and both deflated into her arms. The sound of their weeping and all of their echoes bounced off the tile. Gentle words within Dyane's head reminded her of thoughts she had at home about needing funeral clothes. She might have admitted to her worry with some embarrassment, if asked. Most people wore black to a funeral, but she didn't own a black dress, nor see this as a somber hour. Rather, she viewed the event as a celebration of Sara's life. Up until this moment, they still allowed themselves to laugh, to love, and to remember how Sara celebrated each day. Dyane wanted to focus on those things instead. She didn't want to focus on the dying but on the living. Easier said than done, before the key moment when her mom handed them an envelope of cash, Dyane stuffed her anxiety. She refused to fixate on what she needed for the funeral—it felt foolish to her. She remembered reprimanding herself at home just days before.

Secrets

Why are clothes even an issue? Do you realize how insignificant they are at this moment? She stood conflicted before her mom in the bathroom, sure of one thing, God did care about her need, and His word ministered to her spirit like a rushing wind.

Therefore, I tell you, do not worry about your life, what you will eat or drink or about your body, what you will wear. Is not life more important than food, and the body more important than clothes? Look at the birds of the air they do not sow or reap or store away in barns, and yet your heavenly Father feeds them. Are you not much more valuable than they? Who of you by worrying can add a single hour to his life? And why do you worry about clothes? See how the lilies of the field grow. They do not labor or spin. Yet I tell you that not even Solomon in all his splendor was dressed like one of these. If that is how God clothes the grass of the field, which is here today and tomorrow is thrown into the fire will he not much more clothe you, O you of little faith.

Matthew 6:25-30

At that moment, Sara's secret gift took a rebellious stand against any remaining disbelief Dyane held. She now knew the full truth. Dyane held in her hands more living proof that God cared about her and her sister Elizabeth. Even more exciting, God knew both she and Elizabeth needed something to wear to Sara's celebration of life service. Inspiring Sara with the idea in the first place, He alone prompted and equipped her to follow through. Dyane felt amazed that He loved them so much, so much that He took care of every detail. Even while they cared for her, Sara thought of them, using her to supply for their needs through her part-time job at the bank.

Not only did they feel cared for with clothing, but their family continued to humbly accept meals, toilet paper, and cards that streamed into the Gillespie home. Dyane felt an overwhelming outpouring of love and affection for these people. Their ability to muddle through their own grief, all while caring for them during those days, didn't go unnoticed.

Just after getting Cullen to bed for his afternoon nap, Dyane leaned upon the kitchen counter and sank on the stool beneath it. Joseph, Uncle Allen, and her cousin Christopher bantered with each other on the opposite side of the kitchen counter and perused the delectable spread of food before them. Setting their eyes on dessert first, a container of red gelatin caught their sight. Dyane's eyes widened as they all began to fill their plates with heaping red cubes. She stared at them, trying to search her mind for a memory when either of them had eaten cherry gelatin with such eagerness before. She came up empty and sipped in her breath. With eyes locked in a stare, she closed her mouth as her husband's lips sealed around his own straw. Through their tightened lips, each took turns sucking the sweetened red cubes into their mouths through the long tubes. The race ensued and their muffled laughter mixed with a gathering crowd; another family party broke out before their eyes.

"If Sara were here, she would be right in the center of this craziness," someone stated.

Dyane laughed to herself and thought—*what a perfect way to celebrate her life—a family gelatin-sucking contest. Here's to you, Sara!*

***

That frigid November week, as flurries whipped around the parking lot, Elizabeth and Dyane inched toward the front of the church. Following behind their mom and stepdad, they wore the new outfits Sara paid for. They slowed and stood side by side next to Sara's gleaming casket adorned and surrounded with a heaping array of flowers and plants. As she wiped her eyes, the fragrance dizzied Dyane's head—intoxicating her for a moment. She held her stomach, feeling nauseous. The aroma rooted into her memory. As the odor drifted amongst them, she rubbed her nose and quietly gasped, remembering the day Sara passed away when they smoothed floral lotion upon Sara's skin. The remembrance stung. She wondered—*Were we preparing her body like the woman who poured expensive perfume on Jesus' body for His burial?*

Dyane stared at Sara, appearing made-up and peaceful, lying in the cream taffeta. Paralyzed by the moment, she remembered, just last week Sara chose the mahogany carved box and embellished it with the light taffeta, as the last decision she needed to make. Months before, Sara planned this very day on paper from start to finish and chose to wear the same silk cream dress their mom wore on her wedding day to their stepdad Jim. Everything appeared just as Sara planned.

Dyane noticed her father Gerald push through the glass doors and saunter into the church building with a blonde acquaintance on his arm. Without a smile on his lips, his eyes shifted from side to side while color traveled up underneath his open collar, and the vein upon his neck began to pulse. Dyane caught Elizabeth's attention, and they drifted over to him while he lingered in the open foyer.

Dyane's neck tensed underneath her turtleneck before her father hugged her with his firm arms. His slight smile and embrace felt awkward and rushed to her. The almost obligatory and numbed effort left her hoping for more. Gerald offered a brief introduction to the woman by his side, and then his facial expression became stoic. He glanced at the woman often as she stood in front of him, seeking his gaze. Dyane bit her lip, realizing her father a shell of himself and the woman on his side more of a mannequin than a friend. Gerald guided her through the double doors into the worship area while their arms remained folded around each other. *Her nails appear gripped into his skin like a cat*—Dyane thought, then chided herself for thinking it.

Caught off-guard by the heavy march to his step and edge to his voice. She felt prompted to wonder if he took some medication before his arrival but dismissed the notion as dishonoring somehow. It seemed their father coped with the day of Sara's funeral as best as he knew. His behavior seemed erratic to Dyane. She rubbed under her chin, unsure of her father's reaction once he saw Sara lying lifeless in the flower-draped coffin he paid for. Dyane slipped into the background as he entered into the sanctuary, where the aisle drew him up to his daughter on an ever-elongating road. He gazed upon her at length while wiping his eyes often. He then bent his body over the casket. His chest melted upon her lifeless body and his wet lips kissed her forehead. The tears rained, and his thundering sobs pained Dyane's heart more than she expected. She dabbed the corners of her lids with the wadded tissues she gripped and rested her head upon the wall behind her.

The family stood upon their feet for long hours over the course of two days—embracing, comforting, and loving over seven hundred people that came for Sara's services. In the midst of it all, Dyane and her family saw few opportunities to go to the bathroom or maintain their strength with sustenance. Their endurance did come from somewhere else, though, and she felt as if she walked in a dream. Flower containers and baskets of plants cascaded up the steps behind them and folded around Sara. So many floral arrangements covered the width of the entire front carpeted area of the church. Gardenlike, she welcomed the colorful sprays, a welcome visible relief compared to the barren November trees lining the parking lot. A few hours passed before she peeked between shoulders and caught a glimpse of people extending out of the sanctuary doors. At that, she proceeded to fade out of the room and head toward the library. Food and drinks covered the tables waiting to nourish her family. To Dyane, it almost felt like a stolen moment with her two-year-old son Cullen and a place where she lingered long with him.

Just then, one of their dear family friends rushed into the library distraught, with a tint of red upon his cheeks.

"I felt like I wanted to punch him—I've never felt like that about anyone else before," he confessed.

After a little consoling, Matthew revealed her father's declaration to anyone in the foyer willing to hear him.

"He said—they are all Jesus freaks!"

Dyane grimaced and stared at their young pastor speechless—what prompted her father to say that? She reddened with embarrassment. It became so obvious to her that he lost all of his inhibition before he arrived, maybe even his mind. His soul bared for all to see, grieving out loud and reflecting more recklessness than Dyane knew how to handle. His tongue whipped and lashed those standing near him—uncaring who it cut. She decided no one remained safe from his judgment and made the decision not to stand near him for too long—it felt pointless, almost dangerous. In truth, Dyane questioned his notice or remembrance of either of his other daughters that day.

Those they already spoke with gathered throughout the large pew-filled room as the family reentered. Some stood content without a seat, and some clustered together, sliding into the long rows of pews. The line moved past Dyane and continued its flow into the worship area even after a few more hours passed. The room soon became so full that masses of young adults filed up the stairs and into the choir loft behind her. It almost felt comforting to her in some odd way. Sara appeared surrounded by love, and Dyane took the time to gaze over each face until their images became a blur in her eyes. She knew the same love Sara shared with each of them prompted them come that day. They once looked beyond her baldness, her weight losses and gains, her nausea, and her moments of frailness and would always remain a part of her cancerous journey. Now, here they all sat. Grateful they came Dyane wanted to celebrate Sara's life with them, and she hoped every memory they carried with her sister remained a lifelong treasure.

Secrets

From the front, Dyane saw adult faces lit up with smiles and some that sat expressionless—uncertain and confused. She found that she related to both emotions so well. *My body still aches from my own grief, my mind is tired from thinking about all the details and decisions that have lead up till this day, and my spirit feels on guard. Maybe as farfetched as it is—I do want everyone here to experience at least a smidge of hope and see that God is very real—especially Dad. For those that can't seem to get beyond her physical death today, I pray that even though her flesh has failed, they will find assurance. I pray they will find comfort that she has been made new in heaven...* A flow of Dyane's thoughts confessed as she glanced around the room, and then she sighed. It felt so good to release her tension. Carrying Cullen in her arms and Joseph allowing her to go first, she slid down into her seat and leaned back—desiring to put her feet up. Instead, she passed Cullen over to his daddy, bent her knee, and rubbed it, feeling relieved every creative detail, and every plan came to fruition. Dyane observed the glowing beauty before her, which Sara designed and approved of long before. Dropping her eyes, she prayed everything went as planned.

The trumpet's blast mixed with the other instruments, drums, and voices shook the room with power. It also rattled

Dyane's insides so much that she felt like she celebrated and mourned—all at the same time. The music led her into the hidden corners of who she had become, searching for all that still needed comfort, all that needed more truth, more faith, more hope—all that needed more reason to live within a dying world without her sister.

Sweet babies bounced to the echoing beats from the stage while they hung upon the hips of their parents. It seemed like they all held their children a little tighter that day. *Children, so dependent upon us to live... who are we to be entrusted with their souls, their little bodies—created with such complexity? Each one infused with unique talents and gifts, each with such different personalities, each with ideas and questions that are sometimes too big even for us as parents to answer. Life is so amazing—and so short in breaths. It's as if each one is numbered. Each inhale, each exhale also leads me towards a day like this one. A day that will sum up my life in an hour-long service...* Dyane allowed her mind to wander just a little, remembering all the extended hugs she gave to her family, friends, and strangers today. Extended hugs and deeper conversations, that's what really made the day even more special to her.

Their pastors, Earl and Matthew, led the crowd on a journey through Sara's life. Matthew served as her student pastor, the one that lead her away from where her emotions bent and instead led her to fall in love with Jesus Christ. She fell deeply and welcomed Him as her personal Savior. Matthew, not only her youth pastor, became a family friend who loved like a brother at all times. He then entered into the eulogy as one who grieved himself.

"Sara Dana Schreck was born on May 26th, 1977—" Matthew began. "She had been working as a bank teller at First Savings and Loan of South Holland. She was a graduate of Sandridge Elementary School. She attended Illiana Christian High School, where she received an honorary diploma in 1995. Sara was very active in school, serving as a cheerleader.

At the age of seven, Sara accepted Jesus Christ as her Savior and was baptized along with her sister at Antioch Christian Church, by their Uncle Allen," he said.

"Sara will be remembered— " he began.

Matthew battled to fight the tears. His long pause allowed everyone to succumb to them also. After clearing his throat, he continued. "Sara will be remembered as a beautiful young lady who was always adventurous and full of life and energy.

Her family remembers finding her at the age of two, riding her tricycle down the middle of busy Joe Orr Road. At two and a half, she was jumping off diving boards with her water wings. At the age of three or four, she was already riding a two-wheel bike without training wheels."

At this, the crowd chuckled a soft laugh, as did Matthew. After taking another breath, he spoke again.

"Sara loved school. As an elementary student, she liked being the center of attention with the teachers by helping them as much as she could. She was an 'A' student and always tried to outdo herself in everything she did. Sara idolized her two older sisters, Dyane and Elizabeth, and all her childhood, she tried to catch up to them. When they cheered at Sandridge Elementary School, Sara asked if she could be the school mascot. And then, when she was old enough, she became a cheerleader too.

Sara also loved being involved in activities through the church. She attended summer church camp at Hanging Rock Christian Assembly and at Lake Region Christian Assembly. Through camp at Hanging Rock, Sara learned one of her greatest loves—using sign language. The first song she learned to sign was 'Friends.' One of her favorite things to sign was the phrase, 'I love you bunches,' which she was signing for her family even on the day she died.

In junior high and high school, Sara involved herself in the youth groups at Deer Creek Christian Church. It was common at youth meetings, Bible studies, and Sunday School to find Sara in the front row with her Bible open and her hand in the air to volunteer to read or give a comment. Two weeks ago, I asked Sara what her favorite memory was out of all her youth group experiences. She told me that it was the first time that she was able to go to the Christ in Youth Summer Conference with our high school group, which would have been in the summer of 1991. She said that she felt closer to the Lord there than she had up until that point.

In September of 1991, during her sophomore year at Illiana, the symptoms of her cancer manifested themselves, and her appearance started to change. It was then that her relationship with Christ really changed also. Her payer life escalated. She was confused and scared.

Her diagnosis came in January of 1993—Adrenal Cortical Carcinoma—an eight inches tumor of the adrenal gland which had then spread to the liver. Yet through twelve-course of chemo, eleven infections, four major surgeries, one attempted liver transplant, hair loss, and major sickness—Sara praised God and loved Him with all her heart."

Matthew's voice trailed into sobs. His brotherly love was evident. Composing himself before the crowd proved difficult, he stepped away from the podium, wiped at his eyes, and returned for a sip of water. Everyone joined him; Dyane felt grateful for the pause. Noses blew noses, and she breathed deep with a shudder.

"During her illness, Sara thanked God for the opportunity of extended life that allowed her to see her nephew Cullen come into this world and witness her sister Elizabeth's wedding to Neil Miller, which was so very important to her. She finished her sophomore year, got her driver's license, got a job, and attended her Jr./ Sr. Banquet. When I think of Sara during the time of her illness, I remember someone who was concerned about her family and friends before herself, someone who involved herself in extreme acts of kindness—like selling over 150 pizzas while she was in the hospital this past summer to help our high school youth group go to Christ In Youth in California, and I remember someone whose depth of insight, wisdom, and maturity far exceeded her years.

God used Sara to become an example to us all and to so

many more of whom we may never know. We will miss her because of how she loved us and because of what we learned from her. In her own words, 'I win either way. If I live, I get to be with my family and friends. If I die, I get to be with Christ in heaven.' There is no doubt that Sara is there in heaven right now where…" Matthew said before clearing his throat. "…where she has heard the words, 'Well done, good and faithful servant. Enter into your eternal reward.' As well as these words from God, 'Sara, I love you. I love you. I love you bunches—.'

Earl placed his hand on Matthew's shoulder, and they embraced just before Matthew sat down upon a nearby stage seat. Sara fulfilled her life purpose and every person now knew it while blotting salty tears off of their faces. Sara rested in her casket adorned in her mother's wedding dress as the bride she always hoped to become.

Without any words left to explain or express the emotion of letting her go, Dyane remembered the heartbreaking moment she also let those she loved to go in 1991. She traded them for the journey of a lifetime as a new pastor's wife. Dyane also recalled the moment Sara placed her small eighth-grade school photo within Dyane's palm as she left her young sister waving upon the driveway. Sara said a tearful goodbye while Dyane herself joyfully embarked on her own journey as a new bride. She remembered the new car smell coupled with her sister's written words on the backside of the photo—

"Dyane, I love and miss you a lot! Hope you don't forget me. Thinking of you—I love you."

The grief that day in the pew overtook her again, it made her nose run, and the minimal amount of tissues in her hand failed to collect the ongoing flow streaming her face. *How could I ever forget you, little sister? I will always miss you too... I love you. I love you.* Releasing Sara proved more difficult than she imagined, as did the reality of Sara going to heaven before her.

After the conclusion of the service, Dyane leaned against a wall in the church foyer. Photos pinned upon picture boards sat upon tables where they found life again in viewer's minds. Every photo sparked memories that made some laugh and some swipe over their cheeks until they dried. She slowly began to feel grateful for the happier memories of years past. Just before stepping away from an elaborate display, Dyane reached up and touched both a sweatshirt and a t-shirt hung upon the wall above. Both shirts, covered with colorful messages, served as written encouragement to Sara. She imagined each author at the church that day, feeling thankful they took the time to build up their sick friend. It made all the difference in Sara's journey. *Yes, today was a good day*—Dyane decided.

While Elizabeth and Dyane both said their goodbyes to their father, Dyane contemplated. *Will he be okay? How will he get through this mourning alone?*

Gerald punched the bar on the glass door and held it open for the woman at his side. Dyane caught herself trying to remember her name. As she searched her memory, she struggled. She decided to ask her a second time if she saw her again, but Dyane didn't count on it. The woman appeared for that day's trauma, almost like a blonde shield of protection. Regardless, she knew deep down what she needed to do. Early in her teens, Dyane made the all-important decision; to make the effort to care about the women her father brought by. She thought back then God might use her to show them His love somehow. Throughout her adult years, when women appeared to search for lasting love from their father, she felt empathy for them. His relationship track record rated poor at best. She always felt concern for these women, that a romance with their dad might derail them from an opportunity to love someone more stable, peaceful, committed, gentle, loving, and faithful. The image of wealth that drew them still remained just an image. She hoped over the years God used Dyane, Elizabeth, and Sara to extend His grace and point them toward God. To Him she confessed—*Lord, today, I loved this woman more from a distance. I prayed for her, but I'm sorry, that's all I had the strength to do.*

She then remembered the words from Matthew 22:37-39 that wrenched her heart.

> *Jesus replied, Love the Lord your God with all your heart and with all your soul and with all your mind. This is the first and greatest commandment. And the second is like it: "Love your neighbor as yourself."*

As Joseph pulled their blue sedan up to load, Dyane kept her sights fixed upon her father Gerald's rental car before he drove it out of the church parking lot. Her stomach ached, and after his car disappeared around the corner, she gave her hips a gentle pounding with her fists. She knew she avoided him after his outburst, and she failed to extend love. Dyane also knew she harshly judged the stiff woman by his side, and she didn't offer her any grace. Loving those that loved

Secrets

Sara and extended love to her in return came easy, but she knew God wanted something more. He called her to extend mercy, even when difficult. Unforgiveness kept her light from shining brighter, and she knew it. She felt it and rubbed her collar bone off and on as she placed things by the foyer exit. She accepted the responsibility, the need to step up and be an active part of His plan. She even sensed God drawing His bride, the Church He longed to return for. To shine like Sara, Dyane needed to do something more. Leaving that day, she hoped her prayers modeled Matthew 6:9 b-15, the verses she read the week before.

> *Our Father in heaven, hallowed be your name, your kingdom come, your will be done, on earth as it is in heaven. Give us today our daily bread. Forgive our debts, as we also have forgiven our debtors. And lead us not into temptation, but deliver us from the evil one. For if you forgive men when they sin against you, your heavenly Father will also forgive you. But if you do not forgive men their sins, your father will not forgive your sins.*

Dyane prayed with eyes open in the foyer alone and silent amongst the crowd of family, church family, Illiana Christian High School students and teachers, hospital friends, community neighbors, co-workers, and acquaintances she longed to know more. They all said their warm goodbyes, but she clung to Elizabeth and her mom the longest. Sniffing back the tears, they embraced with lush flowers and plants enveloping their feet. Many people passed them as they exchanged goodbye kisses and recollected their packed bags of display photos and planters. Dyane knew they all played a key role not just in honoring Sara that day, but in her life, in her story, and in her relationship with Christ. Dyane considered, without every single one of them, Sara's story might have lived out far different. God wrote them in it, choosing their role, their function, and their mission in her life. God used each one to help Sara become the godly woman they loved and remembered.

As Dyane's car waited for its turn to pull away from the curb and forward under the awning, she prayed again in the waiting. *I forgive my dad Lord. I forgive him. Please forgive me for my lack of love in my grief, my lack of obedience to your Word, my lack of forgiveness. Prepare my heart, my soul, my mind, my strength to truly love you as you deserve. Thank you for loving me and loving every person that came today—please bless them. Please bless them in their relationship with you forever.*

Secrets

In Jesus' name, Amen.

Cullen waved at her with a chubby hand, smiling from his car seat. His daddy Joseph also extended a soft grin and wave from the driver's seat. Dyane shuffled between the patches of ice and remaining snow on her trek to their car. She returned their love, reflecting a bright but exhausted smile with tears glistening her eyes. Dyane felt free, free to love like she never loved before. She also felt free to truly forgive and accept Jesus' forgiveness and grace in her own life. She often needed unconditional love too.

Joseph surrounded the car and opened the door for her. Receiving the items Dyane juggled within her hands, Joseph also took the opportunity to kiss her before she sat in the passenger seat. The wintery wind still blurred her gaze, yet, she winked at him anyway as he shut her door.

At the age of twenty-four, she looked around herself at the irreplaceable living, breathing gifts from God He placed in her life. She understood now more than ever; she still held opportunities to grow in an intimate relationship with God and love those around her more. Dyane repositioned herself in the front seat desiring to live as a citizen of heaven while she still yet lived. As she buckled her seatbelt, God readied her spirit for the adventure ahead, even if no one understood or she went alone. Dyane lifted her son's blue blanket over his dangling legs, then stared out the window while Cullen's head lowered to doze. Joseph reached for her hand and grasped it within his own.

As they passed countless billboards, she prepared her mind to throw off all the entanglements screaming for her attention. Closing her eyes, she tilted her head back on the headrest. Dyane pictured Sara in heaven, her room made ready, and her body healed. Determined, she remembered to fix her eyes not on things seen but on things unseen, as she encouraged Sara to do. Poised to live out her own God-given purpose, Dyane also aimed to live like she'd die tomorrow and die knowing she'd live forever. Dyane wiped her lashes with a cream-mittened hand. She refused to forget her sister's living example. Resolved, she sat up straighter and filled her lungs full. Dyane twisted in her seat, studied her peaceful son, then up at Joseph's aqua blue eyes as they scanned the bustling traffic before them.

God's call on her own life both surrounded her and waited. It waited, concealed for her yet to discover. While the weighty thought made her feel queasy, Dyane's chest grew heavy, and she allowed her thankful tears to fall. As Sara's mission unfolded three years before, Dyane remembered what God lovingly did with her sister's mustard seed faith and belief. She really did reap what she sowed. Her heart thumped hard; she knew He loved her too. Peering into the sky, she swallowed and sighed. Re-filled with hope, Dyane's accepted His will for her and whatever that might look like. Even though fathoming the future proved impossible, she knew it rested within her Father's hands.

Praise be to the God and Father of our Lord Jesus Christ, the Father of compassion and the God of all comfort, who comforts us in all our troubles, so that we can comfort those in any trouble with the comfort we ourselves receive from God. For just as we share abundantly in the sufferings of Christ, so also our comfort abounds through Christ. If we are distressed, it is for your comfort and salvation; if we are comforted, it is for your comfort, which produces in you patient endurance of the same sufferings we suffer. And our hope for you is firm, because we know that just as you share in our sufferings, you also share in our comfort.

Corinthians 1:37

Chapter 20

Remembering Sara

Sara's family and friends were knit together like few in this broken world. They held together by an unbreakable bond. Though not everyone understood it, this scarlet thread wove through every part of their lives and throughout Sara's as well.

Sara's family chose Jesus Christ as their faithful rock and rescuer because they experienced love and forgiveness they didn't deserve, *also known as grace.* Jesus Christ remained their common, living, unifying thread, and they drew closer to Him together. Instead of isolation in grief at the time of Sara's death, everyone drove long distances without hesitation to hug each other and say a temporary goodbye. They knew their belief, repentance, and confession of Jesus as their Lord and Savior—assured them a great reunion in heaven.

Twenty-six years since Sara's passing, her story remains

timeless to those who embarked on the journey with her. Her story, unforgotten, intensified over the years. Through many seasons and life sufferings of their own, not one failed to remember Sara Schreck. Dyane witnessed some of them wrestle with God in the valleys, especially when terminal illness touched their own lives. While some believed in God or embraced a fake replica, everyone eventually faced a crisis of belief like Sara did, forcing every family member and friend to make a choice.

In honor of her life, each person in this chapter celebrates amongst grief to share their own memories with you. All played a significant part in Sara's legacy on earth. They loved her along the journey through many highs and lows. These words are a treasure trove of unedited reflections and true testimonies written by family, friends, and those that heard about a young girl with cancer. Her story became a section of their tapestry, a legacy, which now surpasses time and generations.

1. Susan (Sara's Mother)

Susan, Sara's mother, decided to share her thoughts, advice, and feelings by writing her grandchildren about their Auntie Sara.

"Auntie Sara's example was her constant faith and trust in her heavenly Father. Her whole being was consumed with Him. She trusted Him, no matter where He led her. She didn't always like the path that she was led to—but she believed that He wouldn't give her any more than she could handle without His help and intervention.

To this day, when trials come my way, I hold on to God's promises—she taught me that. But, I also have to share the fact that her sisters taught me that also. If you want to know Sara, her values, her faith, look to her sisters, for they possess the same. Though all three of them are unique, they all love the Lord with all of their heart and soul.

Auntie Sara was fun, kind, loving, a faithful friend, a beautiful daughter, giving, loyal—a sister and a child of Christ. She was pesky sometimes when she was younger; she could sweet-talk anyone almost out of anything! She wanted her sisters' attention, and she wanted to be so much like them. They didn't always get along, but they loved each other unconditionally, and that's where Christ fits in. If you can't love your brothers and sisters or get along with them, how is it that other people are to see Christ in you? You could just look at Sara and see Him inside of her. Let Jesus shine in your lives, in your choices, towards your friends, but most of all to each other. Hug often, love much, and don't be afraid to let Christ be seen in you! Learn to trust Him... the trials we go through in life will be what draws us closer to Him. That was very evident in Auntie Sara's life. Before cancer, she was so like us now. After cancer, she radiated Him! I know in my own life, if I hadn't had my trials, I wouldn't be at peace with God. I know I have a long way to go, but I know that Jesus is right beside me.

A memory I have of Auntie Sara to this day is hugging her and telling her I didn't want to let her go (from the hug)—but she interpreted my saying that as not wanting to let her go to be with the Lord... She so looked forward to that day—being *home* with the Lord Jesus—when she realized that *He* wanted her home with Him. She became this way because she talked with Him daily, studied His Word, prayed constantly—for His will to be done in her life. Your moms and dads do that so well. Learn from them—you'll see a lot of Auntie Sara in them!

Her sisters, your moms, are what Auntie Sara would have been—maybe a little more adventuresome and daring—but the same love for the Lord Jesus. They all even looked alike! All three girls; Dyane, Elizabeth, and Sara—reflect Christ and His gifts within themselves. Your mom—Dyane writes beautiful praise words from her heart, your mom Elizabeth sings beautiful words with her voice, and Auntie Sara's life and death were praises too, left behind through pictures, videos, and memories. She left those praises for us while your moms fed us with life, words, music, and so much love! All three complemented each other, so if you want to learn, know, or see examples from Auntie Sara's life, look to your moms—they knew her probably better than me. Most important of all, the one to look to for her example and to learn from would be our Lord Jesus Christ—He taught her everything she knew, and she *listened!*

She was also a fighter and motivator. Your More-Poppo kept her picture next to him in his room while he himself battled lung cancer. He knew that if she could fight—so could he! She gave us all hope; when she believed in something, she gave it one hundred and fifty percent. Her greatest loss and sadness were not meeting and knowing you, her later nieces and nephews—James, little Joseph, Grace, Kathleen, Joshua, Rebeckah, Karis, Timothy, Sara, Philip, and Elizabeth. We made a promise that you would all know her!"

2. Jim (Sara's Step-Dad)

"I remember being afraid of the girls when I married their

mother, Susan. On the first day back from our honeymoon, Susan was going upstairs to take a nap, and I had no clue what to do around the three girls. I quickly went outside and washed the car—which was the second time in a two-day time period—they made me so nervous!

I do remember Sara being kind of a brat when she was young. She tried to wrap people around her finger, gain more attention, pushed issues harder, and did goofy stuff. I thought of Sara as the 'wild one,' Elizabeth as the 'quiet one,' and Dyane was somewhere in between.

One of the memories that I have is that Sara always wanted to try and help me with whatever I was doing. One day, she came outside and asked if she could help me with the car. Regretfully, I told her she couldn't. I remember going upstairs to her room afterward and apologizing. Remembering back to that day, I never wanted that to ever happen again. She reminds me of our grandson James, always offering to help me. Sara taught me to always let my grandchildren help!

It took me a while to realize what was going on with Sara when things began. I thought it was a girl thing, and it was no big deal at first. It was all confusing. I don't remember anyone telling us it was cancer until one of the head nurses asked about a port going in for the chemotherapy treatments. At that time, I didn't feel like I really caught on to that or that it really hit home. It wasn't until after the first chemo treatment that it began to all sink in.

One of my saddest memories was sitting in the family room next to Sara while she held her turquoise bowl. After she would throw up, I would run back and forth to the bathroom to dump the bowl out. The second saddest memory was when our neighbor came over and helped Susan give Sara shots. I found out after several years had passed that my boss was supposed to change insurance companies while we were in the middle of treatments—but kept our carrier for an extra one to two years just to make sure Sara's medical expenses were covered. There is a regret that I do have, though; I wish I had spent more time at the hospital with her. I put work too far in front—maybe as a protective measure somehow.

I felt so scared at the time of her liver transplant. It seemed scarier to me than the news about the cancer. I rushed out of work when I got the call, then we waited. We hoped for a long surgery, but then I saw her coming down the hall—so quickly after going in. I felt unsure of what to think. It's like there was hope, and then there wasn't any hope at all. I remember our pastor Earl being really upset with God that day...

I remember a funny answering machine message Sara left about throwing up. I remember she hammed it up on a trip to Washington, DC. We had such a good time on our Hawaii trip too—Sara really loved the ship's 70s dance party! One of my favorite memories, though, has to be the burping contest that Sara, my daughter Christine, son Steven, and I had on one of their visits. We burped into the recorder, and Sara won!

It seemed like two separate lifetimes—before cancer and after. Sara's personality changed, and she gained a different viewpoint. Sara became more serious and became concerned about other people more than herself. There is no question that cancer changed her life and probably helped save her. She became very unashamed about God. I hope my grandchildren will be the same way, without having to go down the same path."

3. Grandma (Sara's Grandma Irene)

"I am not too good at words, but I will try to share my thoughts and feelings for you...Sara, age fifteen, diagnosis—Adrenal Cortical Carcinoma, a very rare type of cancer. Prognosis—not good.

Remembering Sara

The news was devastating; there were many tears of despair and fear. Sara cried out, "Will I die? I don't want to die, Mom; I don't want to die." Sara, her mom, step-father, Dyane, and I wrapped our arms about each other and cried. I wanted to throw up.

My despair changed to cautious optimism after the family talked with the medical team. It was decided by the medical team to combat this rare cancer with extremely high doses of chemotherapy for six-day sets instead of the usual four-day sets. The resulting agony Sara went through was very hard to watch, along with the infections she suffered after each set, some life-threatening.

At the core of it all was an extremely close-knit family that came together to give Sara all our love and support, and at the time of her first surgery, we all met at the hospital to be there for her.

I started by praying fervently for a miracle; I mean heart-wrenching, tearful prayers that God would take this from her. Then it occurred to me that I must not tell God what to do, so I then prayed that He would help me to accept His will for her. From that time on, I was better able to cope.

Watching how Sara's faith grew through all of her suffering I think, was what helped all of us. Near the end, she felt that she w 'would win either way—if she lived, she would get to stay with her family and friends, and if she died, she would get to go home to her Jesus.'

I found strength in doing for Sara… I was fortunate to live in the same house, so was available. I shared hospital 'duty' with her mother, sisters, and her friends—staying with her during the day and sleeping in her room at night so she would not be alone. I also watched her mother perform home nursing for Sara, which astounded me, and under the watchful eye of Maribeth. Kathy did some pretty remarkable things for her daughter.

I could not have survived this ordeal so well had it not been for God above my family, or church family, and all the prayers from churches and schools over the state and country. We were not alone.

We were all with her the day of her death… the whole family again with her and by her bedside. She died in her mother's arms with a smile on her face. While it was hard to let her go, how could we despair in the face of her faith? We cried and laughed at the remembering of her life. She was such a big part of our life, and even today, we miss her terribly. She had an impact on so many lives, without really understanding what it was she was doing that made folks comment about her impact on their lives."

4. Anne (Sara's First Cousin)

"Dear Dyane,

I remember standing in the dining room of your mom's house and overhearing the adults talking to Sara bout the symptoms. 'Are you sure you couldn't be pregnant?' Someone asked her. '*No*, honest,' Sara replied. In my gut, I knew something very wrong was going to happen. I just didn't quite get it.

I then fast forward to sitting beside Sara during one of her chemo sessions as she begged the nurses to let me spend the night with her even though I was too young. I remember the joy I felt for being wanted... trusted by someone I looked up to.

By the letters I have read and the journal entries made, we really loved each other. She treated me like a younger sister and valued having me in her life. Her testimony video makes a trip to my VCR once a year. At eighteen, I watched her speak of faith, eternal healing, and God's power. I couldn't believe that such a physically battered woman, my age, could be capable of such wisdom. I yearned to be like her.

Lessons from Sara's life are great in number. I believe my eyes blur in memory around the time (my) Mom got sick. Suddenly, things Sara taught me about life and death were acting out in my soul. Gradually, I watched my mother's body deteriorate before my eyes while her heart continued to remain full of life and strength.

Did Sara's legacy help prepare me for the new loss in my life? Absolutely. And I carry both women a generation apart through my life today... God blessed my life with an amazing young woman; Sara Schreck will always remain a building block of who I am today."

5. Alice (Sara's High School Friend)

"Dear Ma Gillespie,

I just want you to know how much Sara's life is still impacting mine. I know that you know that her death was in God's plan and design; He used her in so many ways... At the time, He used her to teach me courage to stand up and be bold for God, not to fear death, and not to ask—'Why me?' Today God is still using her death and life to teach me. And

Remembering Sara

I say death because had she lived on Earth the impact in my life would not be the same. God is really showing me how at certain times, I think of Sara—out of the blue—she is on my heart. The day after Sara died, it snowed, and I remember waking up to the most glittering snow I ever saw. Now every time it snows and sparkles, I remember Sara and listen for God's leading.

Having one of my very best friends die so young has given me such a different view on life—not just to treasure this life—but to look to our next. Our true home is not here—we are strangers (upon this Earth), and God is our joy and our goal. How you dealt with Sara's death has impacted me more than I ever thought now that I am a mom. Often, I prayed that I would have strength like you, should God take one of my girls. You were at peace—you have joy and inexpressible peace that transcends all understanding. I've seen God show me that verse in your life, and I am so grateful. So, thank you! Thank you for raising a daughter who feared the Lord, a girl who knew 'whose' she was—thank you for being an example of a godly woman under extreme suffering. Sara's death was not for nothing. God used her to display His glory and the goodness of His plans. I'm sure God will continue to use her in my life as well as countless others. For nothing? For so much more than she knew."

6. Alli (Sara's High School Youth Group Friend)

"....It is funny how timing works... I have been thinking of Sara so much lately, and I actually framed one of her senior pictures and put it in my office. Just for the entire beginning of my RN career, I was involved in early infant loss with mothers, spent much of my time in the NICUS and labor and Delivery Units, I finally said, "I want happy stories." Little did I know that I would find myself working with mostly teenaged girls with terminal cancer or terminal illness (cystic fibrosis, etc.). I have walked the path with many young women now; in each one, I see Sara. I see the strength that she had and the faith that she exuded. Her story and life have become part of 'my' story. I will never forget her telling me that I was destined to help people and that she would be looking down. Someday, when I get to party upstairs with her, I am going to just tell her how much her life taught me and how much it continues to teach other people. Both my kids know Sara and her story (and) her faith..."

7. Beth (High School Friend)

"I got to know Sara only months before her death. For some reason, I believe that God led her to me... My favorite memory was the night of the Spire (yearbook) party. Afterward, I had planned to go out with some friends, but they had already left. Instead, we (Sara and I) picked up slushies and went back to her house, and we looked through the Spire for a couple of hours until about 11:30— probably my curfew. She had so much energy that night and could have kept going for much longer! There had been an article in the Spire that her mom wrote about her. She called her mom a 'booger' for writing it without telling her! It was an awesome night, a month before she died, all she wanted to do was talk about my high school problems. She just wanted normal everyday teenager talk. But yet, she was so ready to die! It was amazing to me! I also remember the wake where her mom comforted me! That really struck me—her family had so much strength and reliance on God. And since having my mom die, people said the same things about my family. I think that God gives you so much grace when going through trials that you endure through them..."

8. Peter (High School Friend and Musician)

"My name is Peter, and you probably won't know who I am unless you find a Volkswagen car key among Sara's things; I was always amazed at how happy and full of life she was when she was the sick one among us (at school)... she amazed me with her strength, courage, joy, the list goes on. I wrote a song about Sara...”

9. Todd (High School Youth Group Friend)

“...Not long before she died, Sara and I made plans to watch a movie at her house, and we decided to watch the movie *Hook* with Robin Williams. We spent half the movie just talking about things, but there was a line in the movie where Robin Williams told his son that he was his happy thought that allowed him to fly. Sara looked over at me with her infectious grin and said, ‘I will be your happy thought.’ Sara died shortly after that day, and I often think of her and the time she and I spent together. Sara holds a special place in my heart, and she is still my happy thought to this day.”

10. Kris (Jim’s Co-worker)

“We often are told to listen for that still ‘still, small voice,’ but many of us never hear it. Some wonder why they are not chosen to do so. I believe that all of God’s children are being led by the Holy Spirit who ‘groans’ for us and is talking to you. I can tell you why I missed it for so many years. I did not shut up and listen! I am here to tell you that I not only listen to it (now), I obey it without question. ‘Why is that?’ you may ask. Because I have learned that the Lord has a sense of humor, and I want to laugh with Him. ‘What does it sound like?' I can't describe it but will say it is a gentle nudging. 'What does it say?' I don't hear it, but, for example, when I am led to think about someone who I haven't thought about for a while, I usually know that I am to pick up the phone and call them. And so it was last week when I called Sara's stepfather—Jim Gillespie.

I have worked with Jim since 1984 and know him to be a hard-working family man. We chatted about many things, and in the conversation, I mentioned Sara. Now we had not talked about Sara for at least ten years, yet it did not feel funny to bring up her name. After the conversation, Jim said, 'You know it is really funny that you should call. It is even funnier that you would bring up Sara.' For a moment, I thought I had brought back bad memories and was ready to apologize. Jim then said, 'My daughter is getting information together and wants to write a book. It will include the story about Sara. She is looking for people to share their memories, and out of the clear, blue sky, you call and talk about her.' Jim and I share a bond in our faith in the Lord, Jesus Christ. So we talked about how He often works *that* way. We were happy that we talked, and I promised to call his daughter for details.

Dyane is an absolute delight. With dogs barking and children wanting attention, she was able to chat with me and describe her vision. As she spoke, I could feel that she was being obedient to God's will. Just like me calling Jim, it may not make (sense) to us until the Lord reveals His plan.

Here is the memory I shared with her:

'I remember Sara's funeral being a very sad event (for me). I remember a thousand people at the church and a very moving service. I admitted to Dyane that I don't remember much else because I was really overwhelmed by seeing such a young person in the casket. But I can describe for you, almost in great detail, the wedding dress she chose to wear as her last, earthly garment. It hit me like a ton of bricks when I saw her. A hundred thoughts went through my mind, and all of them were very sad. My final thought was, *oh my gosh, she knew she would never be a bride but wanted to wear the gown.* It broke my heart.

As the years went by, I would tend to think of Sara at weddings. As I matured in my walk with God, I learned many things. My thought patterns changed, and I started to 'listen' to that still, small voice. I want you to know that I now look back at Sara wearing the bridal gown and 'get it.' She was the bride of Christ going home to be with Him..."

11. Ruth (Sara's Youth Group Friend)

"I don't even remember how I got on the list to spend the night with Sara, but I was ridiculously excited to be able to do so and felt like it was a huge honor. She was always so loving and accepting towards me, and I saw it as an opportunity to bring her a little joy back. I had no idea what to expect. I had never spent the night at a hospital, and I wasn't sure how to be helpful, but she was quick to instruct me. She told me that she just wanted someone to pass the time with, and so we chatted most of the night away. She stopped a couple of times because the chemo made her super sick, and I would hold the bucket while she threw up and then get cool rags and wipe her neck and head off. She would brush her teeth, and we would pick right back up in conversation where we left off. At one point, the night got serious because she told me how sad she was that she was never going to get married or have her own children. I had never talked to anyone who was so open about the reality of death. She told me she wasn't afraid of death, and I just couldn't understand that at the time (I do now, of course). She explained that she knew she would get to spend eternity with Jesus in heaven. At one point in the night, she asked me to read to her from the Bible, and I jumped up and got her Bible and asked what she wanted me to read. Then she said words that changed my life… she said, 'Just read me your favorite verse.' I just sort of sat there dumbfounded. I didn't have a favorite verse. I didn't even read the Bible at the time. I was so embarrassed, and after a few lame excuses, she gracefully looked at me and said, 'That's okay, let's just read my favorite verse.' I was grateful for the redirection, and she directed me to Proverbs 3:5-6, and I slowly read the verse to her. After that, she would tell me another verse, and I would look it up and read it or open her Bible to where she had put a bookmark and read from that point. It didn't take long until we had to pause again, and she had to throw up. We went through the process of cleaning her up, and then she told me she was tired and was ready to sleep. I turned the lights off and 'tucked her in' and then laid down and proceeded to listen to her breathing and the sounds hospitals make at night. I couldn't sleep. I was so challenged by the fact that I didn't have a favorite Bible verse and that I didn't know enough of my Bible to even pretend that I knew a Bible verse. I had grown up in the church. I knew all the stories. I had no idea where to actually find them in the Bible, but I believed they were in there. That night, in that room, next to a beautiful friend who loved Jesus more than any teen I had ever met, I made a commitment to take my relationship with Christ seriously and stop being so complacent in my faith. I have never been the same since. I don't know for sure if Sara's favorite Bible verse was Proverbs 3:5-6, but it became the first verse I memorized and knew where it was. It has been my life verse ever since, and I am forever grateful for Sara and the everlasting impact she made in my life simply by living out her very real faith. I hope this brings you joy today as you read and remember and celebrate the residual impact God made through Sara's obedience."

12. Sherry (Fellow Cancer Patient/Roommate/ Survivor and Friend)

"By definition, a hero is a person of exceptional quality who wins admiration by noble deeds, especially deeds of courage. In my eyes, nothing takes more courage than realizing that death is near and accepting it. Fairness is obviously not an issue when dealing with illness. Observing Sara Schreck's suffering has honestly touched my life. From diagnoses Sara has faced the fact that her type of cancer was considered incurable. As a sixteen-year-old, she learned that cancer consumed her liver and that she had to fight in order to survive. Using faith in God as her source of strength, she conquered many big obstacles, thus amazing doctors. Just as her prognosis was improving, it abruptly took a turn for the worse; I would think that she would be insanely angry and upset. Sara is so spiritual that she is not bitter; she does not want anyone to be sad because she truly believes that she is going to a better place.

Through Sara, the meaning of life has been shown to me in a way I could never have experienced alone. She shared her wisdom with me, demonstrating how God does not give more than one can handle (without His help). Through her, I learned the importance of looking for the ever-present good in every situation and, most importantly, to believe in and rely on God. For me, she is a symbol of great hope for the life to come. I feel blessed to have had the opportunity to know her; under no circumstances did she lose the battle. Sara Schreck has touched so many lives that her spirit will never die. My admiration of her undying strength will stay with me for the rest of my life. Her coming to the point of acceptance has been the greatest act I have ever witnessed. Sara Schreck is and will always be—my hero."

13. Matthew Rogers—Lead minister First Christian Church, Warsaw, Indiana (Former youth minister at Deer Creek Christian Church)

"One of the first times I ever struggled intensely over

the question of why a righteous person should suffer was the illness of Sara Schreck. Sara was a young lady—a high school sophomore—pretty, outgoing, cheerleader, loved Jesus Christ with all her heart, and wanted to please God more than anything. She was a delight. Why her? Why did she need to die as a teenager? Since then, I've had many more times to wonder why…

I remember when Sara's appearance began to change. In particular, I recall one night at our Tuesday Bible study in the library at DCCC when Sara was beginning to feel especially self-conscious. She burst into tears and just melted into a puddle of sadness and confusion. I remember she left the room to compose herself, probably going into the restroom. I think some of the other girls might have gone with her. But when I talked to her after the Bible study was over, she just kept talking about how she was getting so fat, how she looked so big, how her facial complexion was a mess. Generally, she just really felt ugly, which was heartbreaking to hear, and something I don't recall her ever saying before or struggling with. I sort of said what best I knew to say about how we all loved her and how she was beautiful to all of us, and especially to God—being really careful not to say stuff in any way that would lead her to think I had noticed she had changed in any way. It seemed at the time like some typical teenage body change stuff was taking place and that Sara was extremely self-conscious about it like many teenage girls would be. Little did any of us know at the time what was really going on.

I remember her spiritual life-changing dramatically during her illness. It wasn't instantly for sure. But as time went on, and probably right about the time when she lost all her hair, there was a big change in how serious she became about her faith. She always, always had an intense love for Jesus. I can remember that back when she was in Jr. High. But this was different. There as a maturity to her faith, and a boldness about her convictions that emerged. She almost had sort of a wisdom about her, if that isn't too much of a stretch. She was experiencing God in new ways and finding Him to be faithful at every turn. It was something to behold, and I'll never forget it. This is the time during which I remember her frequently telling me, "I win either way." Meaning if she were healed or if God chose to take her home.

I also remember how much she hated missing out on the youth events when she was sick. That was tough to see. I remember Todd being so aware of this. He brought back a t-shirt for her from CIY that everyone in the youth group signed. And I still remember standing next to him as he explained to Kathy Troccoli that she should give Sara a call. I thought he was nuts but look what happened out of that."

14. Dr. Earl Ferguson—Community Pastor at Community Christian Church, Illinois (Former senior pastor at Deer Creek Christian Church)

"It is not the length of your life that counts, but what you do with the time that you have. Some people live to ninety or one hundred years, and aside from the 'stuff' they have accumulated, their lives have made little difference. Others live a long and fruitful life and leave behind them a legacy of faith and good deeds done in the name of the Lord. Some lives are brief, selfishly lived, and leave the world worse or certainly no better than they found it. Occasionally, life is brief, and time makes a real difference. I believe that Sara Schreck was one of those persons. The real test of the impact of a life lived for Christ is when we get to heaven and hear the stories of how someone's life and testimony led to another embracing Jesus as Lord. My guess is that Sara is going to be the subject of many of those stories. She lived with such grace and died with such hope that all who knew her were amazed.

I still remember her leaning over the table at a restaurant in the area and telling Matthew and me that she was 'beginning to really get excited about going to heaven.' She knew that some would not understand, and they will not. Her testimony on TV last week led to one young lady in our church accepting Christ and being baptized. Sara impacted in a positive way all those who knew her, doctors, nurses, family members, school, and church friends. I am in no way stretching it when I say that she impacted more people for Jesus in this brief life than most do in a long one. Perhaps this is why God chose to heal her permanently rather than temporarily.

Thanks, Sara, and 'well done.'"

Chapter 21

A Season Of
Abundant Grace

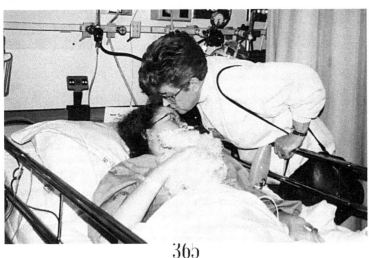

A Season Of Abundant Grace

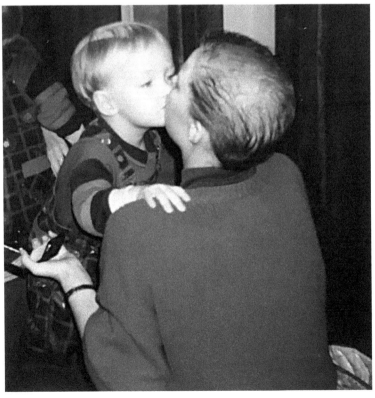

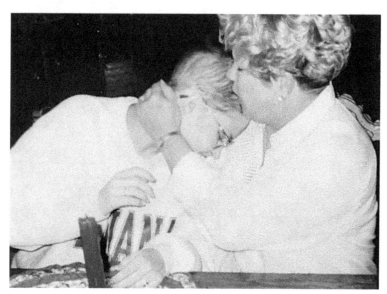

Epilogue

A chuckle escaped Dyane's throat at Joseph's announcement—

"Kids, we're adding something new to our family night
each week—Memory Lane," he announced. A clap of cheers
from six pizza-filled mouths bounced off of the ceiling. Fifteen years passed, their six children scarfed down every last
crust and clamored over one another to dig through old VHS
storage boxes. Dyane lit with a smile but exhaled at length,
noticing the handwritten 1999 date on the cardboard. Joseph
lit the fire, and as Dyane switched off the end table lamp,
its flickers warmed the room. The vintage videotapes had
sat so long in storage, every image behind the television's
glass felt unfamiliar and new. Laughter and giggles explod-
ed as they all began their travel back through time. Kathleen, their eight-year-old, pushed up close to her side, and
Dyane pulled the afghan up over her daughter's shoulders.
Squeezing her tight, Dyane marveled at the filled L-shaped
sofa bending around them. Kathleen, three-year-old Joshua,
ten-year-old Grace, twelve-year-old Joseph, fourteen-year-
old James, and seventeen-year-old Cullen all lined the sofa
and stared, captivated by the memories. Dyane fought the

temptation to scold Joshua as he toddled up to the television screen to press his sticky hands and face against it.

"Joshua, be careful," Dyane said.

Determined, he blew with all his strength toward the four glowing candle images upon Cullen's one-dimensional birthday cake.

The camera panned slow and steady over Grandparents Susan and Jim, Kathleen and Lawrence, as well as Grandma Irene while they sang Cullen's birthday song. A few smiled toward Joseph while recording, and camera flashes bounced about the pale-yellow dining room. Elizabeth sang and rocked from side to side next to Neil while little Aubrey's chubby arms surrounded her mommy's legs and buried her face at the sight of her grandma Susan's camera. Joseph's lens remained on Aubrey as she pressed into Elizabeth's thigh and underneath her mommy's pregnant belly. Cullen blew out his four candles and grinned at his chocolate birthday cake before clapping for himself with the cheering crowd surrounding him. As the images of Cullen's birthday party ended with a flash, Dyane's stomach dropped at what was shown next.

Her father Gerald crouched in their first home, bent at the

knees, and leaning back upon his heels for Cullen to climb onto his back. Cullen balanced upon it, unsure what to do with his little hands.

"Hold on tight, Cullen—here we go," Gerald stated.

Cullen smiled, grabbed at his papa's shirt, and held on for dear life. Both of them swayed from side to side, and he tossed his grandson upward in a series of bounces for added excitement. Like a bronco-busting rider, Cullen steadied himself with each lurch and squealed. Gerald's black dress pants rode up his legs. His covered knees rubbed at the carpet as he scooted around the house chasing a bucking Joseph. Wobbling, James clenched his chubby fingers into his daddy's collar. Both clomped on all fours with two screeching little boys upon their backs. Before long, the shocks from the friction of polyester and olefin added another element of excitement. They all scurried across the eight-foot by five-foot space, down the hall, and through the kitchen, like oversized mice in a maze, every turn created a few logistical issues for the two grown men. Gerald laughed from his belly, and his voice climbed higher. He lost all inhibitions and appeared determined to create the best horsey on the rodeo for his grandsons, not to mention, outdo his son-in-law. A chorus of neighs punctured the air, and their trotting vibrated across the carpeted flooring until James fell off his daddy with a thud to the floor. Upon landing, he tipped his head back, crying and whining about returning to his saddle. The video camera quivered, and Dyane overheard her own voice through the speakers. Her inability to stifle giggles lifted her smile in fire-lit darkness again.

Surrounded by their illuminated children while the vintage family video shook from time to time, Joseph didn't hold back his delight. The wrinkles next to his aged eyes deepened, and his contagious laughter encompassed the room. With every unwrapped memory, his body bobbed up and down. A lump in Dyane's throat enlarged, began to ache, and pressed in deep towards the back of her neck. She reached up and swiped at the corners of her eyes with hopes no one would see or ask, "Why are you crying, mom?" Yet, her eyes refused to shift away from the images of her father Gerald during his last visit to Chicago following young Joseph's birth.

On one hand, her heart swelled with unexpected comfort and peace, yet it also felt as if it split in half within her chest. She rubbed where her heart ached. Dyane absorbed the flashing memories as rainfall on the parched ground— her husband and father admired by their two miniature men.

Epilogue

Captured in time, she observed both make a lasting investment, far more than any gold watch now sunk somewhere in the Pacific. His grandchildren, his loving two daughters, and his son's-in-laws became his absolute delight.

Dyane remembered witnessing her father's sorrow find its comfort and hope upon the birth of Gerald's first four grandchildren. They all wrapped him tight in unspeakable joy. No greater happiness or pride filled her father more than when his arms embraced little blonde squirming bundles resembling his daughters. A quiet study of their tiny faces always made him beam. As he revealed his new role as a grandfather and visited their first home, preschool sons Cullen and James fixated upon him. Minty gum often stuffed their mouths, the aroma of aftershave, as well as their laughter; all permeated the air while the three of them watched a thrilling movie about vegetables. Those times clung to her mind as some of the best memories of her dad before the accident, which stole his life.

Yes, she still grieved, but on nights like this one, she felt more joy than expressible. On this evening, gathered together with Joseph and her growing children beside her, Dyane looked to her right again through the amber-hued darkness. The glows from the television reflected off of Cullen's face, he laughed from his gut, and his eyes twinkled with light. As he recalled his papa's playfulness, Cullen's joy spilled. She wanted her son to pack these good memories into his mind as he shipped off to boot camp the following year. Seventeen years had slipped by way too fast.

Joseph announced their children's bedtime with a press of the remote. While he instructed James to shut off the video player, protests from their smaller children ensued. Unrattled, Joseph and Dyane stayed their course through the rebellion. They shooed them off to bed with prayers, kisses, and goodnights, but after they left, Dyane sat still and longed for more. Without a word, precious memories slid back into the video box. She wiped away tears with the back of her hand. Dyane's last memory of her father's visit added to her heartache, and at the moment, she tried with everything she had to remember his voice. *Hi Dyane—! How's my little mama feeling? How are the boys?*

The memories ministered to her spirit while she clung to Joseph. She began to breathe deep and swipe both palms over her eyes again. Joseph broke their silence.

"Honey, you miss your dad?" He asked.

He ran his fingers through her long hair, and her shoulders

dropped. She sniffed but couldn't meet his intense blue eyes for too long before closing them again. Joseph knew. He guided Dyane tight to himself and prayed over her. Dyane joined him and finished with a few more silent prayers of her own. *Thank you, Jesus, for Joseph's prayer, these memories I still have with my dad, and the opportunities to show your love. That's it. It's over. It's all over—oh Lord Jesus, in your mercy, I pray he's with you now.* His lifetime—simplified, condensed, and in his daughter's mind, swept away all too soon. Like many, Dyane knew much loss. Nevertheless, she still held tight to the goodness of God's grace. In the midst of loving and remembering those gone before, it took memories like this to remind her—joy still comes in the morning.

Dyane held onto hope that her children cherished the brief pixilated images of their papa's life with Cullen and James. She also hoped in the future; smiles appeared at the mention of his name. A papa remembered not by what he owned or strove for, but by the moments he engaged, the moments he loved as they always hoped and prayed.

Afterword from
Kelly D. McManus

Thank you for reading *Till That Day Comes*; I truly hope you felt immersed in the outpouring of God's grace as you read this based on a true story novel. I pray this story drew you in and it continues to remain with you long after it's set on your bookshelf or you share it with family and friends.

Sara Schreck and those who supported her all endured their own critical moments and faced mountains of choices. Nevertheless, most pressed on with living hope and faith. Breath by breath in Christ, often with tear-streaked faces, they overcame great obstacles by God's grace. They lived out their call. They did not give up.

At times, we all wonder about the closeness of God, yet we must believe the living Word of God still speaks and satisfies our greatest need, even in our greatest troubles. Sara found this true. God gave her bold faith and courageous obedience through the power of his Holy Spirit and the guiding light of his living word. Sara was never alone.

381

Till That Day Comes

In the Bible, John 3:16-17 says:

> *For God so loved the world that he gave his one and only Son, that whoever believes in him shall not perish but have eternal life. For God did not send his Son into the world to condemn the world, but to save the world through him.*

For anyone who believes, repents, and is reborn through the act of baptism into Jesus Christ, He gives His promised Holy Spirit. This offer of new life extends to anyone willing to receive it. A life that holds meaning, purpose, mercy, peace, and a promise of eternal rest with Almighty God. Oh, what fellowship, joy, and hope remain for those who follow Him!

You hold in your hands a story based upon true events as well as true testimony. While their journeys swirled with pain and joy in the midst of grief, this family learned that God still works all things for the good of those who love Him.

Today, you may need endurance and wisdom as you contemplate your own tough situation. In this light, I pray you will always remember, choosing to live every day as if it is your last day and knowing you will live forever is possible but must begin with faith in the one who loves you most. He is our living hope.

By His Abundant Grace,
Kelly

Acknowledgments

To Sara's friends and Illiana Christian High School, thank you for allowing God to use you in the mightiest of ways. To the Deer Creek Christian Church family—thank you for your prayer support at just the right moments. Matthew Rogers and Dr. Earl Ferguson, how we thank you for the biblical truths you taught us by how you lived and loved.

Thank you, TBN and Trilogy Christian Publishing, for your God-given vision and the teamwork it required to offer this book for such a time as this. Also, Mark, Kaycee, and the Trilogy team, I'm so grateful for your commitment to this project, you are all such a blessing!

Re-Frame Ministries and Dr. Nederhood, thank you for being used by God at Sara's critical *Why Me?* Moment, it blessed her faith beyond measure.

Thank you, Kathy Troccoli, for your support and the beautiful part you played in encouraging Sara.

Make-A-Wish, thank you for giving Sara and our family memories that we still cherish today.

Till That Day Comes

To my cherished journey mates, and By Grace sisters—Jane, Tina, Bonnie, Kristy, Wanda, Cindy, Hannah, Susan, Julie, Suzy, and Sheila. I love you all; thank you for your steadfast prayers and encouragement throughout my writing journey.

To my mom Kathy and dad Jim, thank you for your powerful prayers, your countless sacrifices, your encouragement, and long-suffering. To my mother-in-law, Sharon, and father-in-law Larry, thank you for your encouragement and for allowing God to use you. To my "whole family," may we never forget our journey together or our bond. To my sister, Amy, may you always remember the significance of your God-given joyful song in Sara's life and mine. Family, I love you all!

Finally, to my greatest gifts and treasures upon this Earth—to my husband Lawrence, thank you for awakening to God's will for *Till That Day Comes* and the books on our horizon. Thank you for becoming one of my biggest cheerleaders; none of this would have been possible without you! To our faith-filled children Conlin and daughter-in-love McKae, Caleb and our daughter-in-love Maria, Micah, Naomi, Jostlin, Lauren, Nathaniel, Ellyana, Reed, and our precious grandchildren, Evangeline, Josiah, Oliver, and Felicity (plus

Acknowledgements

every cherished future McManus clan member we've prayed for), thank you for calling me mom, for your prayers, the laughter, the sacrifices, and sometimes the necessary pressure to get it all done.

May our family and all our outrageous adventures continue to point to the amazing grace of God. I love you all!

However, I consider my life worth nothing to me, if only I may finish the race and complete the task the Lord Jesus has given me—the task of testifying to the gospel of God's grace.

Acts 20:24.

Enjoy more from Kelly D. McManus at:

KELLYMCMANUS.COM

TILLTHATDAYCOMES.COM

There are simply too many beautiful souls to mention throughout *Till That Day Comes* to do anyone's role justice in Sara's story. If you knew her, you know she loved you with everything, and our family loved you also. You may still remember better than any, so we hope you will reach out to us by sharing your own testimony and about God's grace in your life through this story!

CPSIA information can be obtained
at www.ICGtesting.com
Printed in the USA
LVHW010442180821
695512LV00012B/268